TRANSFORMING
Birmingham New Street

Our partners

The Birmingham New Street redevelopment project was delivered by Network Rail and funded by Network Rail, Birmingham City Council, Department for Business Innovation and Skills, Centro, the European Regional Development Fund and the Department for Transport.

We're also very pleased to have had the wholehearted support of the Birmingham Chamber of Commerce, Birmingham International Airport, as well as, Arriva Trains Wales, CrossCountry Trains, London Midland and Virgin Trains, who operate rail services from New Street.

Network Rail delivered the Birmingham New Street Gateway project. Network Rail is the strategic lead for the railways in the UK and owns and operates the rail infrastructure across the country. More people use the railways than ever before and Network Rail is investing £38bn over the next five years to expand and improve the railways. The New Street Gateway project is at the heart of these plans.

Birmingham City Council is the largest local authority in the UK and placed the New Street Gateway project at the heart of its Big City Plan for Birmingham.

The Department for Business Innovation and Skills is the regional development agency for the West Midlands. It was established to transform the region through sustainable economic development. The Department for Business Innovation backed the New Street redevelopment as a catalyst for growth, which will create over 11,000 jobs and deliver over £2bn of transport and wider economic benefits to the West Midlands.

Centro, the West Midlands Passenger Transport Executive and Authority supported New Street Gateway as a core element of its plans to continue to develop public transport across the West Midlands.

The New Street Gateway project was developed with the support of European Regional Development funding.

The Department for Transport's aim is transport that works for everyone. DfT is working to deliver a transport system which balances the needs of the economy, the environment and society. The DfT supports transport projects across the English regions. It backed the Birmingham Gateway project and its potential to transform a major rail hub, make a real difference to the travelling public and help to regenerate a central part of England's second city.

TRANSFORMING
Birmingham New Street

 working in partnership with

lilypublications.co.uk

Copyright © 2015 Lily Publications.
All rights reserved.

ISBN 978-1-907945-91-5

No part of this publication may be reproduced,
stored in a retrieval system or transmitted in
any form or by any means, electronic,
mechanical, photocopying, recording or
otherwise, without prior permission in writing
from the publisher.

Produced in the Isle of Man
by Lily Publications Ltd.

Acknowledgements

This book was compiled and edited by Richard Kirkman
Designed by Ian Smith

Photography provided by:

Andrew Fox
Simon Howes
John James
Richard Kirkman
Paul Painter

Centro
Mace
Network Rail collection
Pallasades collection

Foreword – Sir Albert Bore 07

Introduction – Rachel Groves 09

History of New Street Station – Richard Kirkman 16

1960s Rebuilding 32

Funding the Project – Rob Flavell 40

Last Days of the 1960s Station 47

Designing New Street –
    Carol Stitchman & Alejandro Zaera-Polo 54

Delivering the Project – Martyn Woodhouse 62

Sustainability – Azhar Quaiyoom 104

Centro and Birmingham Gateway – Geoff Inskip 110

The Station Manager's Perspective – Steve Lewis . . . 116

John Lewis 126

Pallasades to Grand Central – Jonathan Cheetham . . 131

Destination Stations – David Biggs 135

Looking Back – Chris Montgomery 138

The Contractors 144

CONTENTS

The new north west station entrance on Stephenson Street with a Midland Metro tram linking the station to Birmingham Snow Hill and Wolverhampton.

Sir Albert Bore
Leader of Birmingham City Council

Birmingham New Street Station has undergone a magnificent transformation to become a vibrant, spacious and bright transport hub suitable for our city, and for the people of Birmingham to be proud of. The old station was almost universally disliked, with very little natural light and underground platforms accessible via a dated concrete shopping centre – it was in desperate need of modernisation. It was no longer fit for purpose for the 140,000 passengers who passed through it every day, more than double the number it was designed to accommodate when last rebuilt in the 1960's. As the busiest station outside London and the biggest interchange station in the country, the station was a major constraint to economic growth and regeneration within the city, and region.

New Street has now been transformed from a dark, dingy and overcrowded place into an iconic landmark that is an appropriate gateway to the city. This has all been achieved whilst keeping the station fully operational throughout the development and overcoming a number of engineering challenges. Managing such a huge redevelopment whilst hundreds of thousands of travellers passed through it each day as 'business as usual' should not be underestimated. It is has been an incredible achievement and credit is due to all of those who worked hard to make this possible and to keep our city moving.

Perhaps one of the most noticeable changes is the creation of the atrium which sits in the heart of the building. This enables a wealth of natural light to flood through the building, into Grand Central shopping centre and down onto the station concourse below, through an area almost the size of a football pitch. Creating this effect required the removal of over 9000 tonnes of concrete from the centre of a building located in the heart of the city. This was a huge engineering feat. Over 95% of the concrete that was removed has been recycled for use on other construction projects.

The station redevelopment has been a key project for the city, stimulating economic growth and regeneration and, with the added creation of Grand Central, has provided one of the best-connected retail spaces in the country. This is sure to have a catalytic effect on further regeneration of the city centre and attracting businesses to Birmingham.

These changes sit within the broader context of an evolving city centre emanating from the Big City Plan which was launched in September 2010. This sets out a 20 year vision for Birmingham's City Centre, supporting transformational change to create a world class city centre delivering sustainable growth, improved connectivity, authentic character, environmental quality, new residential communities and a diversified economic base. By 2031 Birmingham will be renowned as an enterprising, innovative and green city that has undergone transformational change in both growing its economy and strengthening its position on the international stage. The development has also provided a gateway to opportunities for many Birmingham people. There have been over 3,000 construction jobs created, including over 115 apprenticeships.

The transformation of the Grand Central centre from the former Pallasades has been an integral part of the redevelopment. With its impressive stainless steel facade wrapping around the entire building, Grand Central makes a significant impact on the city and is a key element of Birmingham's ever improving retail and architectural landscape. Grand Central boasts one of the biggest John Lewis stores outside London alongside a range of other shops, restaurants and cafes and further strengthens the city's position as a leading retail and leisure destination in the UK. Additionally the advent of Grand Central has generated over 1,000 jobs in retail, customer service, hospitality and catering. Importantly most of these opportunities were taken up by Birmingham residents who were previously unemployed.

Birmingham New Street has transformed rail travel for millions of passengers and now provides a unique shopping and station experience. The result of the development is a bright, modern 21st century focal point for the city that will deliver world class transport integrated with premier retail that the citizens of Birmingham can be proud of. This is an exciting time and shows that Birmingham has a lot to look forward to.

Sir Albert Bore
Leader of Birmingham City Council

Introduction by Rachel Groves

Rachel Groves

Birmingham New Street is the eighth busiest station in the UK and the busiest station with the greatest number of passenger interchanges outside London, with a train movement in or out of the station every 37 seconds. It lies at the heart of the rail network with destinations as far afield as Aberdeen, Penzance, Holyhead and Bournemouth which can be reached without having to change trains.

Back in 2010 the station was showing the strain of 50 years without development. The station manager had to close the station doors to the public at very busy times as there just wasn't the capacity to handle the number of people trying to get through the small concourse and down onto the platforms. Around this time over 140,000 passengers used the station every day, over double the number it was built for in 1967. The completion of the upgrade to the West Coast Main Line in 2008 saw increasing numbers of business and leisure travellers leaving their cars at home and taking the train. Today there are over 170,000 passengers using the station every day; something had to be done to meet this ever growing demand.

In addition to overcrowding problems, Birmingham New Street was facing numerous other issues which were being highlighted by the public, media and stakeholders around the city. The 1960 structure was dark, unwelcoming and provided poor access for passengers. In short it did not provide a good first impression of the UKs second city.

Since the early1990s when Sir Simon Rattle championed the building of Symphony Hall, and Brindley

Birmingham's pioneering industrial history is commemorated by the statues of Matthew Boulton, James Watt and William Murdoch in Broad Street.

Queen Victoria looks towards the Council House, designed by Yeovil Thomason and opened between 1874 and 1879.

Right: The former Midland Hotel - now the Burlington - opened in 1874 and faced the railway owned Queen's Hotel across Stephenson Street. The Hotel was transformed by a £20m refurbishment, re-opening in 1996.

Far right: The Hyatt Regency Hotel towers above Gas Street basin and the rebuilt 'Worcester bar', where goods were once transferred between canals in the centre of the city.

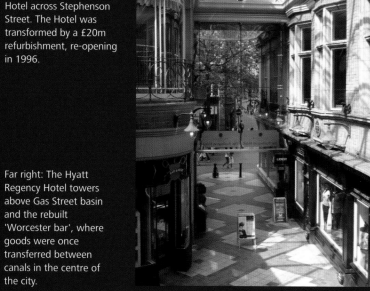

Place and the ICC came into being, Birmingham has been working hard to change the negative image the City had been tarnished with. Over the past 30 years the City has seen a transformation both in architecture and reputation. Juxtaposed against a predominantly Victorian cityscape spawned by Birmingham's proud heritage as a leading light in the Industrial revolution, was a hotchpotch of 1960s concrete structures which were highly celebrated at the time of their creation, but rejected by many in recent years. Since 2000 the Mailbox, Bullring, Matthew Boulton College, the Raddisson Blu, the Cube and the much celebrated Library have come into being as architectural beacons in the City. This coupled with big refurbishment projects such as Fort Dunlop and the Rotunda, the aging structure of Birmingham New Street Station was becoming increasingly apparent.

The concourse was considered dark and tired. It was sandwiched between two huge concrete slabs meaning no natural light could enter the building from above. The first slab lay over the tracks and platforms; British Rail sold the air rights above the station in 1968 for construction of the Birmingham Shopping Centre, later the Pallasades. This unusual upside-down structure with the main weight at the top of the building resulted in the station lacking natural light and over the years has felt darker and darker as the building has aged and the absence of light has become increasingly evident.

Birmingham New Street was considered a concrete block for another reason: it inhibited access across the city centre from one side to the other. As a station it is unique in being located at the heart of Birmingham's city centre, but rather than facilitating easier access the design made it impossible to walk across the city without taking a long deviation around the station, or walking through the shopping centre and descending into the station and exiting the other side. As well as being very inconvenient for residents and confusing for visitors it made a regeneration difficult on the south side of the City.

At platform level the station has 12 through platforms, but in practice it operates with 25 platform faces. Each platform has an 'a' end and a 'b' end and platform 4 has an additional bay creating platform 4c, but as volumes of passengers grew so levels of frustration grew with the cramped station site. The sub level platforms were covered by a seven-acre concrete deck, supported by over 200 columns. This concrete deck makes up the concourse area and dispersal bridge with a further deck above forming the

Built on the site of a former railway goods yard, the Mailbox was originally the Royal Mail sorting office for Birmingham, opening in 1970. Converted to a shopping centre, hotel, restaurants and apartments in 2000, the Mailbox reopened in 2015 after a major refurbishment.

The International Convention Centre (ICC) is a truly world-class venue and one of Europe's most high profile conference centres, welcoming over 350 events and more than 300,000 delegates each year.

Pallasades shopping centre. The 1960s structure gave poor access to platforms with only one dispersal bridge within the station building; Navigation Street Bridge, a second dispersal bridge built as a fire escape in 1991, provided extra access to and from the platforms, but only served platforms 2-11, and did not connect to the main concourse.

Rebuilding the station was never going to be easy.

The inverted structure of the entire building was very unusual and restricted the opportunities to design a new station. The railway lines and platforms run underground and are constrained laterally by buildings and the street pattern, and vertically by the building support pillars. The foundations of the Bullring, which was rebuilt in 2003, and the buildings to the north east constrain the number of approach tracks to serve the 12 platforms. With only two pairs of lines running in and out of the station the number of trains which can access the platforms is restricted and the surrounding buildings preclude future growth.

The surrounding buildings also created issues for undertaking any type of heavy building work. The station is surrounded not only by a thriving city centre but also a telephone exchange, four hotels and a myriad of residential buildings. To the north lies the Burlington Hotel and Premier Inn, and to the south visitors can stay in the Comfort Inn or the Holiday Inn. Any demolition work was going to need careful planning and an extensive consultation process.

But by careful planning and a phased approach there was minimal disruption

Future Systems' iconic architectural design of the Bullring Selfridges store set a new standard for Birmingham when it opened in September 2003.

The Library of Birmingham, the largest in the UK, opened in September 2013. Designed by Francine Houben of Mecanoo, the distinctive building was shortlisted for the 2014 Stirling prize for excellence in architecture.

The Piccadilly Arcade was built as a cinema in 1910 and converted to a shopping arcade in 1926; the distinctive period shop fronts survive.

Birmingham's extensive canal system has been exploited as the heart of an extensive urban regeneration programme.

for people using the station. The project team managed to keep the station operational throughout the project allowing passengers to catch their trains as normal.

20 September 2015 will remain a very special date as it marked the day when the people of Birmingham finally got a station they could be proud of. The passenger experience for the thousands of people who use Birmingham New Street every day was transformed. Passengers could finally enjoy a bright, modern 21st century focal point for the city and a world class transport hub – one that passengers and the people of Birmingham and the West Midlands deserve. And the opening of Grand Central and John Lewis as part of the station redevelopment further enhances the city's reputation as a prime retail destination.

In these pages you will see how this remarkable feat of engineering was achieved and meet some of the dedicated individuals who had the vision to create the station we see today.

The 81m high grade 11 listed Rotunda has been a centre-piece for Birmingham since it opened in 1965.

The final phase of the Mailbox development, the Cube was designed by Ken Shuttleworth of MAKE architects and opened in 2010.

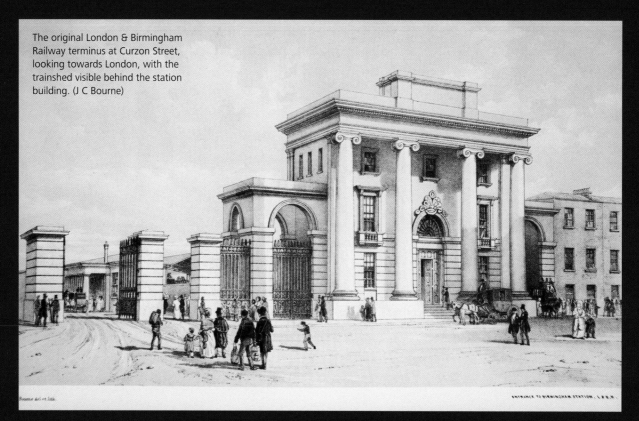

The original London & Birmingham Railway terminus at Curzon Street, looking towards London, with the trainshed visible behind the station building. (J C Bourne)

Curzon Street station today looking towards the city; the trainshed was originally in the foreground.

History of New Street Station by Richard Kirkman

'The connection of Birmingham with London was most important; the population of the former was extending with its business. between 1751 and 1831 it had increased from 50,000 to 110,000. Its trade had more than proportionately improved. Its fine products were celebrated all over the world. Its mechanical power was almost marvellous. the most trifling trinket and the most ponderous machine issued from its factories. In half a century one hundred and sixty-nine steam engines had been created. With all this the mode of carriage had not greatly enlarged. The shortest journey by canal – then the only mode of sending bulky articles – occupied three days. More than a thousand tons came weekly, and business was shortly lost for want of more rapid communication'.

J A Francis

**A History of the English Railway:
its social relations and revelations 1820-1845 (1851)**

Richard Kirkman

At the start of the nineteenth century, Birmingham was well established as 'the workshop of England' and was prominent in the development of the growing canal network. Like other prominent towns and cities it was being transformed by rapid population growth and industrialisation, based on the traditional industries of brass, gun manufacturing, jewellery and button making.

The earliest railways in Britain were purely local affairs, but the authorisation of two trunk railways on 6 May 1833 laid the backbone of the future system.

The Grand Junction Railway can be traced back to attempts to link Birmingham and Liverpool as early as 1823, but these early schemes were thwarted by opposition from canal proprietors and landowners. The final route left Newton le Willows, on the Liverpool & Manchester Railway, and headed south through Crewe, Stafford, to the east of Wolverhampton and through Aston towards Birmingham. The London & Birmingham Railway route was also influenced by the opposition of landowners, resulting in, for example, the construction of a lengthy tunnel at Watford to avoid local estates. The route was characterised by substantial engineering works, including Kilsby Tunnel and Tring cutting, which added substantially to the cost.

George and Robert Stephenson designed both railways, and initially planned to meet head-on to permit through running. Land was selected at Nova Scotia Gardens, a lightly populated area to the east of Birmingham, thereby avoiding the cost of heavy earthworks and the purchase and demolition of property. The London & Birmingham would approach from the east, with the Grand Junction meeting it from the north after tunneling through Gosta Green. The latter proved a difficult and expensive option and met with opposition from landowners, notably James Watt at Aston Hall. By now Joseph Locke had been appointed engineer of the Grand Junction and he surveyed a new route in a long arc from Perry Barr to Nova Scotia Gardens, which were now approached from the east. Parliamentary powers were approved for this alignment.

Meanwhile the London & Birmingham pressed on with their plans and selected a site on the south side of Curzon Street for their terminus. This site was constrained by Curzon Street, canals to the south and west and New Canal Street. This left little room for the Grand Junction station, which was squeezed in to the north of the site. The Grand Junction approached their station over a 28 arch viaduct from Lawley Street and was the first to operate, albeit from a low key opening on 4 July 1837, when trains terminated at a substantial temporary station at Vauxhall (now Duddeston), as the new terminus was a long way from completion and passengers were forced to take a coach transfer. Goods trains followed in February 1838.

The London & Birmingham Railway was opened in stages, with the line from Birmingham to Rugby

18

The adjacent hotel has long gone, but Curzon Street station is still an imposing structure. Millennium Point now occupies the site of the Grand Junction station buildings.

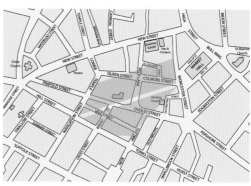

The site of New Street station superimposed on the original street pattern. Construction of the station resulted in the removal of a large number of slum properties.

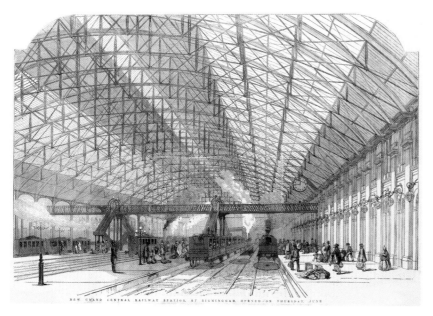

The impressive overall roof of the original 'Grand Central' station on opening of the station. At the time it was the largest span of its kind in Europe, only later surpassed by St Pancras. (Illustrated London News)

The Stephenson Street entrance to the station lay through the collonade beneath the Queen's Hotel.

opening for goods traffic on 12 November 1837 and passengers on 9 April 1838. With the opening of the full length of line on 17 September 1838 it was possible to travel by train from London to Liverpool, halving the 11-hour journey of the fastest coach. Shortly afterwards the link between Vauxhall and Curzon Street was completed by the Grand Junction, opening on 19 November 1838.

Joseph Franklin of Liverpool designed the Grand Junction terminus. The front elevation comprised *'a handsome central building supported by two corresponding wings, (which) exhibits a total length of about 700 feet to the street. There are two entrances for the convenience of passengers arriving and departing by the trains, with spacious gateways belonging to each for the passage of carriages of all descriptions'*.

The London & Birmingham commissioned noted architect Philip Charles Hardwick to design their terminus stations. He envisaged a central building to double as a hotel, flanked by lodges, with the west and east-facing frontages boasting 45ft Ionic columns – of *'austerely elegant design'* (Pevsner) – to counterbalance their more famous Doric cousins at Euston. The main arrival and departure platforms lay behind the building with a 217ft roof, with two 56ft 6in spans – 'one of the finest in the world'. Messrs. Grissell and Peto built the structure for £26,000.

Railway Clearing House map of Birmingham 1914.

Interchange between the two railway companies involved the tortuous shunting of coaches between the two stations, and it was not long before it was agreed that northbound through trains would use the Grand Junction station and southbound services the London & Birmingham. 15 minutes was permitted for passengers to take refreshment and the hotel provided the first permanent refreshment facility in a station building. The popularity led to the extension of the hotel facility as early as 1840, albeit destroying much of the architectural integrity of the original plan.

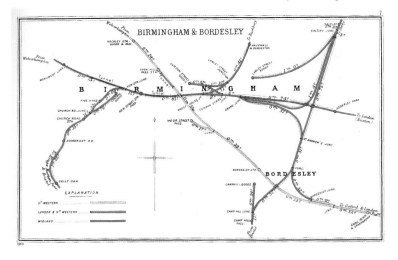

Both companies designated their stations as 'Birmingham', the use of Curzon Street not being made until November 1852.

Routes south west

The docks at Gloucester were another magnet for early railways, having been linked to Bristol by a horse-drawn tramway from 1834. The Birmingham and Gloucester Railway opened to Curzon Street – by agreement with the London & Birmingham – on 17 August 1841, joining the established line at Gloucester Junction on the approach to the terminus. Through traffic to Bristol and the South West was hindered by the change of railway gauge at Gloucester and it was many years before a common gauge was adopted. The Birmingham & Gloucester Railway was taken over by the Midland Railway on 3 August 1846.

A Route east

The London & Birmingham line linked to a branch from Hampton-in-Arden to Derby, but proposals for a more direct line from Stechford to join this route came to naught. A branch was planned from Whitacre to Birmingham to overcome the need for through services from Birmingham to the East Midlands to reverse at Hampton-in-Arden, and this direct line opened on 10 February 1842. The new line terminated at Lawley Street, considerably further from the city centre, and at a much lower elevation than the established railways making interchange difficult and laborious for passengers, for whom a footpath was constructed.

Amalgamation and intrigue

The railway network developed by market forces, and the Grand Junction supported an embryonic Birmingham & Oxford Junction Railway, as a means of curbing the monopoly of the London & Birmingham on the area south of Birmingham. Whilst this support was a ploy to force the London & Birmingham to negotiate merger terms, the scheme nonetheless received Parliamentary approval, which included provision to sell the operation to the Great Western Railway. The new line was planned to terminate at Snow Hill with a branch to Curzon Street; by the ploys of nineteenth century railway politics these options were reversed and the Birmingham & Oxford was forced to build a viaduct from Bordesley towards Curzon Street, even though it would be impractical to form a junction with the London & Birmingham. The resultant half-mile viaduct still stands, never having seen a train.

Meanwhile the Birmingham & Oxford Junction was in discussion with the Great Western on amalgamation but failed to reach terms, and a chance meeting precipitated agreement to rent the line to the Midland Railway Company. The emerging London & North Western Railway – an amalgamation of the Grand Junction, London & Birmingham and Manchester & Birmingham companies, which was formalised on 16 July 1846 – discretely supported this.

Routes north

The political maneuverings to open up the territory south of Birmingham were matched by similar attempts to outflank rival companies to the north.

The Oxford, Worcester & Wolverhampton was authorised in 1845 and the Grand Junction and London & Birmingham promoted rival schemes to open routes to Shrewsbury and Chester. The London & Birmingham reached agreement with the Birmingham Canal Navigations and a nascent Shrewsbury & Birmingham Railway

Looking down Navigation Street towards the site of the new North West entrance. The edge of the overall roof is visible and the Midland Hotel now faces the Queen's Hotel across Stephenson Street.

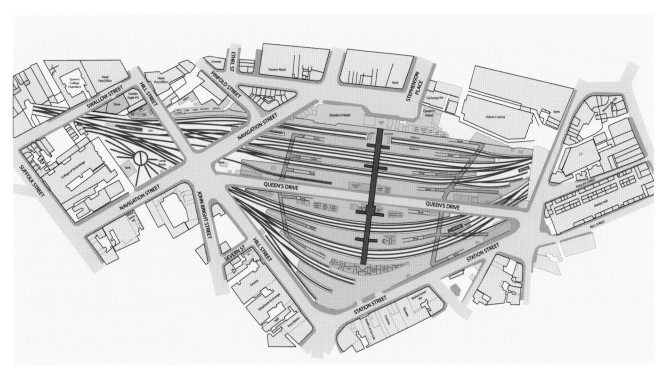

Birmingham New Street around 1923.

to build a line to Shrewsbury with branches to Dudley, Stourbridge and Stourport. The Birmingham, Wolverhampton & Stour Valley Railway (BW&S) was formed in October 1845, just a week before the initial agreement to form the LNWR.

By now the London & Birmingham was promoting a 'Grand Central Station' for Birmingham and the BW&S proposed to build a line from Bushbury through Wolverhampton to a junction with an extension of the London & Birmingham at Navigation Street. Powers were approved in August 1846, but the branches to the Stour were thrown out in the House of Lords. Although never reaching the Stour, this route into New Street is still known to railwaymen by this name.

The LNWR had no intention of allowing the Shrewsbury & Birmingham access to its proposed terminus and obstructed the development of the line at every opportunity, including denying access to Wolverhampton station and forcing the S&B to build a temporary terminus. The S&B turned to the Great Western (which had control of the Birmingham, Wolverhampton & Dudley line) for help, and eventually amalgamated with that company. The LNW retaliated by making very slow progress in constructing the line from Wolverhampton to Birmingham. A lengthy standoff ensued with the line completed but closed and the route from the outskirts of Wolverhampton to Shrewsbury operating, but with the S&B denied access to Birmingham. The Stour Valley line remained dormant until goods services commenced from Monument Lane in February 1852 and it was not until 1 July 1852 that the first LNWR passenger trains operated. The S&B was still not granted permission to use the line and its first trains did not run until 4 February 1854. By now the Great Western was close to completing the Birmingham, Wolverhampton & Dudley line, and the S&B services transferred to Snow Hill from 13 November 1854.

On to New Street

The location of Curzon Street was an inconvenient half-mile outside the centre of Birmingham, and almost double that distance by road. Further it was very remote from the northern and western aspects of the town.

As early as 1838 the Street Commissioners had proposed to build a 'Railway Boulevard' to link directly from New Street to the station, but plans were scaled down as local opposition mounted and costs grew.

Whilst the early railway approaches favoured the easterly location of the station, there was a belief that a more centrally located site would be more beneficial than building separate stations elsewhere, as was happening in many other cities. Sites at New Street and Snow Hill were considered but the former was a clear favourite given better proximity to the main civic buildings. The Snow Hill site was to be utilised by the Birmingham & Oxford Junction railway. On 28 August 1845 the London & Birmingham agreed to extend its line to New Street. The new location encompassed an area of some of the worst slum properties in Birmingham in a wild and lawless area known as 'The Froggery'.

The Bill for the new station and extension of the railway from Curzon Street received Royal Assent on 7 August 1846, shortly after the formation of the London North Western Railway Company. A number of conditions were imposed, including a requirement for the station to be roofed over and a restriction of use to passenger trains. Prophetically it was recognised that the station could become a barrier to free passage from one side of town to the other and the company was required to 'at all times maintain through, under or over the said station, in the line of King Street a passage for the convenience of foot passengers, which passage shall be other width not exceeding 12 feet… and shall be kept open to the public and in repair and lighted at such times and in such manner as the said Commissioners shall approve of, at the expense of the company'.

The King Edward's School also exploited its position on New Street (later the site of the Odeon cinema), securing agreement to purchase any land affected and part of Peck Lane adjacent to the school. The Governors were gifted prime real estate for their benefit, including the future site of Exchange House. At the same time the unsavoury properties nearby were to be eliminated.

The Act stipulated that construction should be completed within three years, but was eventually to take seven. The station was variously referred to as 'Navigation Street' and 'Grand Central', but in November 1852 the name 'New Street' was determined.

The compulsory purchase included The Froggery, Peck Lane, Queen Street and King Street, three churches – The Chapel, The Welch Chapel and Lady Huntingdon's Church – as well as the Old Meeting Houses of 1689 and 1795, a synagogue and cemetery. The bodies were exhumed and moved to a new resting place at Granville Street, where they later found themselves alongside the Birmingham West Suburban Railway. The estimated cost of the works was put at £400,000, with £80,000 being paid for land belonging to King Edward School.

Clearance commenced in 1846, but the 'underground' nature of the site involved the excavation of 25 feet of earthworks, which slowed construction. At the same time the Stour Valley route was extended eastwards from Monument Lane, which necessitated constructing an 845 yard tunnel. This was the first part of the development to open – as far as a temporary station accessed from Navigation Street on 1 July 1852. The line continued across the construction site to provide through running to Curzon Street.

The new station was formally opened on 1 June 1854 when LNWR services were transferred from Curzon Street, which then closed to passenger services, remaining as a goods depot. The Midland Railway diverted trains from Curzon Street on 1 July 1854.

The eventual cost was of the order of £500,000, but this created a spectacular new landmark. An overall glass roof 212ft wide and 840ft long reaching a height of 75ft above the rails spanned the platform area between Navigation Street and Worcester Street; half as big again as the largest span of the time at Liverpool. In comparison the later span at St Pancras is 31ft wider, but 151ft shorter. The roof was designed by E A Cowper of Fox, Henderson & Co of Smethwick, better known for construction of the Crystal Palace. Aris's *Birmingham Gazette* was moved to consider 'the vast structure merits the distinction of being the finest railway station in the world'.

The topography of the area dictated that, whilst the platforms were some 25 feet below New Street on one side, they were level with Station Street on the other. There were four through platforms and two through running lines, together with a symmetrical layout of two east-facing and two west-facing bay platforms. A central footbridge maintained the obligatory right of way whilst providing access to the platforms. Turntables were provided to aid shunting of coaches. Two track tunnels took services out to east and west, although trains for the north had to exit from the east as the Grand Junction and Stour Valley lines only met at Bushbury.

Bradshaw's Guide provided a vivid description of the new station: -

'Situated in New Street, Birmingham, the entrance is at the bottom of Stephenson's Place, through an arcade, to the booking offices for the respective railways; passing through these we emerge on a magnificent corridor or gallery, guarded by a light railing, and open to the station (but enclosed by the immense glass and iron roof), from whence broad stone staircases, with bronze rails, afford access to the departure platform. We then stand on a level with a long series of offices, appropriated to the officials of the company, and a superb refreshment room, divided into three portions by rows of massive pillars, annexed to which is an hotel (the Queen's).

The interior of this station deserves attention from its magnitude. The semicircular roof is 1,100 feet long, 205 feet wide, and 80 feet high, composed of iron and glass, without the slightest support except that afforded by the pillars on either side. If the reader notice the turmoil and bustle created by the excitement of the arrival and departure of trains, the trampling of crowds of passengers, the transport of luggage, the ringing of bells, and the noise of two or three hundred porters and workmen, he will retain a recollection of the extraordinary scene witnessed daily at the Birmingham Central Railway Station'.

In 1854 the LNWR purchased a strip of land on the northern side of the station to enable Stephenson Street to be constructed, although the finances of the company did not enable completion of this work until 1872. The powers did not give permission to open out the land separating the station from New Street, so the Company was unable to exploit the full potential of the site.

Completing the railway jigsaw

The South Staffordshire Railway opened up a route between Bescot and Walsall on 1 November 1847 and, in conjunction with the LNWR, began a service between Curzon Street and Walsall. Further extensions to Wichnor – to connect with the Midland Railway – opened on 9 April 1849, and to Dudley on 1 March 1850. Cannock was reached in 1858, before the SSR was leased to the LNWR from 1 February 1851.

The opening of spurs off the Stour Valley line at Smethwick on 1st April 1867 and Dudley allowed the LNWR to offer direct services to South Wales from New Street. Meanwhile the Redditch Railway opened up a branch from Barnt Green in 1859, extending to Evesham in 1866, whilst the Midland Railway offered services to Nuneaton and Leicester after the opening of the line from Whitacre on 1 November 1864.

The northern arm of the Cross-City line was created when a branch opened from Aston to Sutton Coldfield on 2 June 1862, which was extended to Lichfield in 1884. Finally the Harborne Railway opened a branch line from Monument Lane on 10 August 1874.

The Worcester & Birmingham canal suffered badly when the Birmingham & Gloucester Railway opened in 1841. The company made several unsuccessful attempts to improve their situation by promoting railway schemes or seeking to merge with the Birmingham Canal Navigations. Eventually a route from Kings Norton along the banks of the canal to a terminus at Granville Street was opened on 3 April 1876, by which time the company had been taken over by the Midland Railway. By now New Street station was undergoing a major expansion, and the Midland Railway appreciated the value of being able to run services through the station by constructing an extension from the west end of the station to join the new line near Church Road. This opened as the Birmingham West Suburban Railway on 1 July 1885.

The Midland Railway extended the old formation north from Granville Street crossing under the canal to create a 'Central Goods station' in the area now occupied by the Mailbox and Stanier House. This opened in stages as considerable property demolition was required, being finally completed on 1 June 1892.

The growing volume of business attracted by the railway created congestion problems and the two-track approaches to New Street station were proving inadequate. A cut off line from Stechford to Aston was opened on 7 September 1880, followed by one from Soho to Perry Barr South Junction on 1 March 1888. These permitted goods trains and some passenger services to avoid New Street. The addition of a south curve at Soho from 27 March 1889 allowed services to Walsall to depart from the west end of the station, thereby easing congestion to the east.

Extending New Street

As the number of lines feeding in to New Street station grew, so the increasing volume of passengers placed more strain on platform capacity and facilities. Small changes were made to widen platforms and reconfigure the bays, and the central footbridge was widened, but it was clear that more needed to be done. In 1875 the LNWR obtained powers for an extension of the site to the south into an area of residential property. Initial works opened out the tunnels at each end of the station to widen the station throat and improve operations.

The plans for the station were completed in 1880 and work started the following year. The footprint of the station extended southwards over Great Queen Street, eliminating properties in Vale Street and Bread Street, and now being bounded by Hill Street and a new Station Street, which opened in autumn 1883. Great Queen Street was renamed Queen's Drive and became a carriage road serving the station, although it effectively split the new station into two halves.

The existing platform configuration remained intact and four new curved through platforms, with two central sidings were provided on the south side of the station. A parcels dock in the east and an array of sidings on the south west side of the station completed the new facilities. Two semi-circular roofs covered the extension. The size of the station had been doubled to 14.5 acres at a cost of around £500,000, with around 8 acres being roofed. The LNWR remained landlord of the station and the Midland Railway the tenant, with the former funding the capital works of the station enlargement and the latter the interest on this sum.

Two subways were provided at each end of the station with ramps up to the platforms. That at the western end continued up to the Post Office sorting office between Hill Street and Pinfold Street.

The new platforms came into use from 8 February 1885 and when the Birmingham West Suburban line came into use on 1 July the Midland Railway was able to operate services directly through the station for the first time. Initially services were operated from the most convenient platform for each company, but from 1 October 1889 Midland Railway trains operated from the new side of the station, with LNWR services using the older platforms.

Interior of the LNW station looking east, showing the overall roof to good effect. Note the footbridge forming the public right of way through the centre of the station.

The LNW side of the station from the south. The subway in the foreground is for luggage use only. No 3 signal cabin sits above the central footbridge.

A 1911 view of the central footbridge and No 3 signal box, with a plethora of advertising to distract passengers.

Six signal boxes were provided to manage the operation. The bottleneck at the east end of the station was relieved by the construction of two additional tunnelled tracks to the south of the existing tunnel, which opened in August 1896. This allowed the LNWR and Midland Railway to operate virtually independent services in the two halves of the station. The works were funded jointly by the companies and from 1 April 1897 New Street was declared a joint station, to be managed by a committee made up of equal representation from both.

The 'open' central footbridge made ticket collection difficult, with trains stopping at Monument Lane and Banbury Street on the approaches to the station for the purposes of ticket examination. From 1 July 1885 Banbury Street was closed and examination carried out at Saltley, Stechford or Vauxhall. New Street was to remain a barrier-free station until the 1960s rebuilding. The multiple entrances to the station resulted in a requirement to have three sets of double ticket offices ('main line' and 'local'), whilst five refreshment rooms and three dining rooms were provided across the platforms.

The Queen's Hotel

The success of the hotel operations at Curzon Street and Euston encouraged the LNWR to build a new hotel as part of the New Street complex, although it was not part of the original plans. It comprised the northern frontage of the station facing New Street, approached through Stephenson Place and Station Approach. Access through to the station was provided by archways set in the centre of the building. It was named after the hotel in Curzon Street, which closed when the Queen's opened in June 1854.

The joint ownership of the Queen's Hotel is evident in this postcard issued after completion of extension works in 1917. The station roof is visible, as are some stylised tram and road vehicles.

The Queen's Hotel and station entrance looking along Stephenson Street from the Exchange Building, now the site of the ramp access to Grand Central.

With a frontage of 314 feet, the hotel boasted sixty bedrooms, first and second class refreshment rooms for the station, a coffee room and smoking room, and was soon being advertised as *'one of the finest and most spacious in the town'*. The hotel was leased to its manager, Walter Scott from 1858.

June 1872 saw the name changed to the 'North Western (Queen's) Hotel' as a pre-emptive measure to stop a new hotel being constructed across the road being given the North Western name. in the event this became known as the Midland Hotel (although it had no relationship with that company) and is now the Burlington Hotel, although the Midland name is still preserved in the external stonework. The Hotel name was reversed to the Queen's and North Western and the LNWR took over management from the end of 1881.

In October 1911 the LNWR authorised a rebuilding of the west wing of the Hotel, with 94 new bedrooms and enhanced facilities including banqueting, smoking, writing and billiards rooms, and further improvements were made between 1914 and 1917. The LMS added two storeys to the top of the centre block which opened in March 1925.

Competition

Competition for the traffic between London and the West Midlands reached a peak as the 20th century dawned, with the LNWR accelerating services to match the investment of the Great Western Railway on a new shorter route from London to Banbury which opened in 1910. Euston was now just two hours away from New Street by the fastest trains. At the same time there was an unexpected change in the pattern of local travel, with a growing emphasis on commuting, which had been unknown before the 1890s. This led to an increase of over 50% in the numbers of local trains in the morning and evening peaks between 1890 and 1910. But this created a capacity challenge, as the 1895 rebuild had not been planned with this concentrated traffic in mind. Not only were there increasing numbers of passengers crowding the platforms, but there were also large volumes of non-railway users of the over bridge thoroughfare across the centre of the station. the two groups did not mix well.

Plans to make alterations to the station to address this problem were thwarted by the outbreak of war in 1914. The works would have included a second footbridge through the station and the linking up of the Stour Valley and South Staffordshire bay platforms. The footbridge would have permitted the station to become 'closed', avoiding the need for a stop for ticket inspection on the approaches to New Street.

Recovery from wartime conditions and the stress placed on the railway network, took time and the LNWR and Midland Companies were weakened by the conflict and the inadequate compensation arrangements put in place by the government. The 1921 Railways Act merged Britain's railway operations into four large companies; the LNWR and Midland Railways becoming constituents of the London, Midland and Scottish Railway Company (LMS).

NEW ST. (L.M.S.) STATION, BIRMINGHAM.

Looking straight down Queen's Drive from the Navigation Street/Hill Street road junction showing the contrast in roof styles between the two halves of the station.

Plans for a second footbridge were overtaken by the City Council's ambitions to improve cross-city connectivity by building a new road to link Corporation Street with the Bristol Road; this would have cut through the Queens Hotel and taken out much of the station roof. However the plan had the effect of stalling other works on the station whilst different iterations were considered by the Council. The plans were eventually dropped in 1929.

Minor changes to the station included the installation of electric lighting in 1924 and a public address system in 1935. A more ambitious scheme to replace the 1880s manual signalling with an electric colour light system and embryonic ideas to redevelop by building a raft above the station were put on hold when war intervened in 1939.

During the Second World War the station experienced another dramatic increase in traffic, but also came under attack. A succession of air raids caused extensive damage throughout autumn 1940 and spring 1941. The LNW roof took a direct hit on 28 July 1942. The lamp block at the west end of platform 1 was used as an overnight dormitory for troops in transit.

The station roof was covered in hessian matting to prevent passengers being injured by falling glass and stray light from the station being seen by bombers. When this was removed in 1945 it was evident that the roof on the LNW side of the station was suffering from both structural damage and neglect. The iconic overall roof was removed at a cost of £100,000 by February 1947, being replaced by utilitarian platform canopies using up surplus wartime emergency stock of steel. At the same time the opportunity was taken to resignal the LNW side of the station.

Work to replace the Hill Street overbridge was begun in 1943 as it was in a parlous state, but it was not completed until 1951.

In 1945 the Railway Gazette noted that *'Of our larger stations it would seem that none would have a better claim for early attention than Birmingham (New Street)'*. At the LMS shareholders meeting in March 1946 the company announced that New Street would be one of the stations to be rebuilt when post war conditions allowed.

In 1954 the station celebrated its centenary with an exhibition of historic rolling stock from a 17ft royal saloon dating back to 1842 to LMS 4-6-2 No 46235 *City of Birmingham*.

The 1960s reconstruction

The 1955 *Modernisation of British Railways* Plan included proposals to electrify the West Coast Main Line between London Euston and Manchester and Liverpool. Plans to rebuild New Street were announced on 15 March 1957, and there were extensive discussions with the Council to co-ordinate the work with other developments in the city.

Birmingham at this time was going through a post-war renaissance, with completion of the inner ring road system and the opening of the Bullring Shopping Centre. Changes to New Street were planned

A selection of views of the old New Street station in its last days before the 1960s reconstuction.

to support these civic developments and exploit the large station footprint at the heart of the city. In March 1960 the first plans for the new structure were completed by the British Railways Regional Architect W R Headley. The rafting over of the station and creation of a shopping centre and entertainment complex were at the heart of the proposal, together with a 21-storey block of flats for Birmingham City Council. A new hotel would be built to replace the Queen's Hotel. Allied developments at London Euston and Manchester Piccadilly formed further elements of this modernisation programme.

Birmingham was still served by twin routes from Euston and Paddington and, in an era of rationalisation, it was decided to focus services on New Street as a cost saving measure and as part justification for the electrification programme. Snow Hill was still very busy – in 1964 it saw 7.5 million passengers compared to 10.25 million at New Street – but its main line services were designated to be withdrawn, albeit it was to be heavily used as an alternative route during the electrification programme. Changes were made to infrastructure at Wolverhampton to enable services to work to New Street.

In June 1963 Railway Sites Ltd (a British Railways subsidiary) and City Centre Properties Ltd formed a joint company to deliver the redevelopment of the site above station level. The plans were published in March 1964, but these excluded a replacement for the Queen's Hotel. A pioneering aspect of the plan lay in the use of escalators to access the platforms from the concourse.

The £4.5 million station scheme presented the opportunity to completely reconfigure the station track layout and replace the Victorian arrangement, whilst a further £3.8m was earmarked for the shopping centre development. The station investment was expected to yield a return of 0.1%, with the shopping centre returning 15%, giving an overall yield of 7%.

The project unearthed large parts of the basement of the former Queen's Hotel behind platform 1 during the rebuilding.

The station is complete by 1968, but work has yet to begin on adding the Shopping Centre, although the access ramp is well advanced on the western side. Note the pedestrian access to the 'mousehole' entrance across the station roof.

The scheme had to be delivered whilst the station remained operational, so the plan envisaged the closure, re-construction and re-opening of two platforms at a time. The elimination of Queen's Drive from the centre of the station created the possibility of building 12 through platforms, 11 of which were capable of accommodating 13 coach trains. Work began at the end of 1963 with the connection of the LNW bay platforms to provide new through platforms. The main contractors, C Bryant & Son, began work on 27 April 1964 by demolishing platforms 10 and 11 on the Midland side of the station; by December 1965 the new platforms 6-12 were in use, with platforms 4-5 joining them in February 1966.

The Birmingham Shopping Centre is now complete above the station in this view of the eastern entrance c1970.

There were still up to 400 diesel trains using the station each day, so a sophisticated ventilation system with 62 fans was fitted above and alongside the tracks. Above the new layout a 7.5 acre pre-stressed concrete deck was constructed, supported by 200 columns set in pairs at 36ft intervals. These columns were founded on piles driven down to the bedrock, up to 30ft below ground level. The second level raft incorporated the Birmingham Shopping Centre and the cross-station thoroughfare.

The track layout changes necessitated the reconstruction of road bridges over the station throat. The Navigation Street bridge in particular required two new southern spans, incorporating a special beam 167ft long and 15ft deep which needed a runway to be built adjacent to the Hill Street boundary wall. A similar approach was adopted at the Worcester Street end of the station.

The electrification works included the resignalling of the station area and the construction of a new signal box, which at the time was one of the largest signal interlockings in the world. Designed by Bicknell & Hamilton and W.R. Healey and completed in 1965, the rugged utilitarian structure is now a Grade 11 listed building. It came into use between January and July 1966, replacing 62 manual signal boxes.

The Queen's Hotel survived until 31 December 1965, being demolished early in 1966.

The station was still in an uncompleted state as the World Cup unfolded in the summer of 1966, but the new concourse opened on 9th October, together with vehicular access from Smallbrook Queensway. The overhead wires in the station area were energised at the end of the month, with the first electric services operating from 5th December, and a full timetable launched on 6th March 1967. This date also signalled the end of Snow Hill as a main line station, with the withdrawal of all but the local commuter services.

One of the unrealised proposals for the 1960s rebuilding, with a large tower block sitting directly above the platforms.

Only fragments of the original station remained, notably in the 'Lamp Block' on the west end of platform 1, which was to survive until the recent transformation project.

Although the new station was open it was far from complete. Access from Stephenson Place involved a climb up a temporary staircase from street level. a walk along the station roof as the Shopping Centre had not been built, then a descent through 'a hole in the wall' (later the 'mousehole') to concourse level and further walk down to the platforms. This led to some colourful exchanges in the House of Commons.

On 12 June 1967 Victor Yates opened a debate on the withdrawal of Snow Hill services with a swipe at the new facilities at New Street, stating *'It is beyond my comprehension how planners can plan a station in this way'*. Secretary of State to the Minister of Transport, John Morris, countered that *'the Board has done a magnificent job in producing a right up to date major terminus which accords so well with the new spirit of that great city'*. But Perry Barr MP Christopher Price observed *'it is one of the worst station designs I have seen in Europe... in.. the British public lavatory tradition – and it is a very bad example of that'*. Meanwhile, Baroness Brooke of Ystradfellte complained in the House of Lords about the turnstiles in the station lavatories – and that it cost 6d a time to use the facilities.

By summer 1967 a range of facilities were in place. The included an innovative 104-seat *'Toreador'* restaurant – with bells on each table to attract service and staff using side-rail mounted trolleys – complemented by the *'Taurus Bar'* and *'Pieman'* light refreshment counter, a range of shops and the first UK station off-licence. The station was the first in the country to accept credit cards.

The Post Office moved their city centre sorting operation to a site in Severn Street, and a new tunnel was built under the street at a cost of £200,000 to provide a link to the existing subway at the west end of the station. The tunnel is still in place.

Above the station, Exchange House was completed in April 1968. Designed by Cotton, Ballard & Blow, the 10 storey development included shops at street and upper level and 8 floors of offices. The 94 shop Birmingham Shopping Centre opened in February 1970, completing the redevelopment of the station.

Remnant of the 1960s – this light box survived from the opening of the station in 1967 through to the current rebuilding.

After the tragic Kings Cross fire of 18 November 1987, New Street was classified as an underground station. This necessitated the fitment of fire detection and sprinkler systems and the installation of fire doors at platform level which was completed by July 1991. A new emergency escape bridge serving the west end of platforms 2-11 and exiting into Navigation Street was added in the same year, and this proved a popular exit for commuters.

This was to be the last major change to New Street for nearly two decades when the station underwent its most dramatic transformation.

1960s REBUILDING

Above: Looking across from the Queen's Hotel over the central footbridge; the Midland station overall roof contrasts with the more modern post war awnings above the former LNW platforms. A fine selection of vehicles are parked close to early demolition work on Queen's Drive.

Below: Early work on platform 12 and the hinterland area on the south side of the station, whilst normal station operations continue on adjacent platforms. The Midland roof has been trimmed to faciltate the works.

The overall roof on the Midland side of the station has been removed, and Queen's Dreive is no longer a through route for road traffic. Semaphore signalling is still very much in evidence. Platform 12 is not yet ready to receive its first passengers, and temporary awnings are being erected on other platforms.

A Redditch bound DMU threads it's way through the debris, as track is being installed at platform 12. Mailbags litter the platforms as passengers take a keen interest in the works. The overall roof is reduced to a central spine and contractor's cars are parked on the last vestiges of Queen's Drive.

Below: The view from the Rotunda shows work well advanced on platforms 10-12, and early works on what would become platforms 6-7. Two pedestrian walkways are maintained across the site; the former LNW platforms are still relatively untouched, as is the Queen's Hotel. In the mid distance the future site of the Mailbox is still a railway goods depot.

More traffic disruption at the Navigation Street/Hill Street junction as the bridge works continue.

The route of Queen's Drive is just visible through the centre of the station as work is under way on platforms 6-9. The Rotunda is already a landmark of the Birmingham skyline.

The changing panorama from the Queen's Hotel as construction proceeds above platforms 10-12 and a pair of diesel multiple units creep through the site. The pedestrian link is maintained, somewhat precariously, across the building works.

The western subway under construction using a 'cut and cover' approach. Mary Poppins is playing at the Futurist Cinema.

Above: Passengers on 'The Cornishman' service from Penzance to Bradford get a close up view of demolition work. The venitilation system is being installed as the main concourse structure rises above the platform slab.

Right: The frame of the concourse roof takes shape above the platform deck, whilst the road access to the Western entrance nears completion. Pedestrian access through the site is increasingly precarious.

Below: Demolition work under way adjacent to the Queen's Hotel in the area now occupied by platforms 1-3. In an era marked by a different approach to Health & Safety, the guard's van in the foreground has acquired a coating of sand.

The last remnants of the central footbridge survive as construction proceeds through the mid numbered platforms. The service spine is now formed above platforms 10-12, as the escalator stuctures are built either side of what became the main dispersal bridge - broadly in line with the original pedestrian footbridge.

The raft has now reached the central platforms, with the access ramp to the Birmingham Shopping Centre in the foreground. Ventilation components and a motley collection of builder's huts are scattered on the roof.

Good use is being made of rail equipment as a steam crane lifts a concrete beam into place above the east end of platforms 7 and 8. New Street No 1 signal box stands in the foreground, with No 2 on platforms 10/11.

Two railway cranes working in tandem lift a concrete beam in place, with the Queen's Hotel in the background.

A Cricklewood based steam crane prepares to lift a large beam into place at the west end of the station.

39

Looking down from the
Rotunda, Queen's Drive
has gone and the access
from Smallbrook
Queensway has yet to be
built. The works are
particularly intrusive at
track level.

Demolition work proceeds on the
Queen's Hotel on the future site of
platform 1. Rail wagons are in use,
but the track has attracted a
significant volume of debris.

FUNDING

An early perspective of the south side entrance, when two tower developments were proposed adjacent to the site.

Looking north across the concourse from the upper level.

Funding the Project by Rob Flavell

Rob Flavell
Director, Turner &
Townsend Project
Management.

The initial aims of the Gateway Project were to modernise and update the existing station building and its associated facilities, to accommodate increased passenger capacity, reconfigure and improve the Pallasades Shopping Centre, enhance the surrounding public realm and provide a landmark development to significantly contribute to the status and continued regeneration of the City Centre and the wider West Midlands region.

Proposals for three main built elements – the station building, reconfiguration of the Pallasades Shopping Centre and two proposed tall buildings on Station Street – were granted outline planning permission on 4th July 2007. Significant improvements were also proposed for the public realm and the general environment surrounding the station site.

The project was seen as a significant regeneration opportunity to be a catalyst for the continued transformation of the city centre and the wider region by securing and facilitating significant public benefits for Birmingham to enhance the economic, social and environmental well being of the city and its citizens.

New Street station was designed for passenger capacity at a time when rail use was declining and the use of the private car was increasing. But growth in the use of the railways – particularly since the 1990s -meant that peak passenger flows regularly exceeded station capacity. Indeed, the station currently caters for twice the number of trains and passengers that it was designed to accommodate.

The Pallasades Shopping Centre was built above the station and the station concourse following the 1960's reconstruction of New Street Station. The shopping centre retained its original layout, contrasting starkly with the modern retail developments of the Bullring, the iconic Selfridges building and the Mailbox.

Stephenson Tower, completed in 1967, lay in the southern area of the station off Queens Drive; Network Rail owned the freehold and Birmingham City Council a long leasehold interest in the 20 storey block which contained 80 flats.

In 2002 a scheme of sequential station improvements was developed, but these were rejected as they failed to address passenger capacity issues. The Strategic Rail Authority (SRA) created a Masterplan to resolve capacity and overcrowding. However, following stakeholder consultation and analysis, it became clear that the rail industry could not deliver the scheme without significant external funding support. The focus of the Masterplan on station issues failed to address key stakeholder concerns of pedestrian connectivity and permeability, public realm improvements, modal interchange, external station appearance, the Pallasades Shopping Centre and wider regeneration benefits. No funding was allocated and the Masterplan was not progressed.

The Masterplan was presented at a New Street conference at the Council House in July 2003. The SRA advised that no funding was available for the Capacity Masterplan Scheme, so Birmingham City Council undertook to lead a review of options for a scheme to address all stakeholders objectives. At a Birmingham Forward event in summer 2003 the SRA formally invited the City Council to become Project sponsor.

The Council created a Birmingham New Street Steering Group including Birmingham City Council, Advantage West Midlands (AWM), the SRA, Centro, Railtrack (now Network Rail), the Mall Corporation (then owner of the Pallasades One), the Birmingham Alliance, the Birmingham Chamber of Commerce, the Mailbox, and associated professional advisers.

Over 2003/4 a series of options were explored. A wider group embracing the business community, and chaired by Alan Chatham of the Mailbox, undertook a 'Blue Sky' study. A proposal to close the station for two years to allow a comprehensive re-development of the site and the surrounding area was discounted as the impact on the operational railway and the city was significant and the scheme unaffordable.

A further report built on the Masterplan Scheme and the Blue Sky study. This aimed to develop a holistic scheme, combining passenger capacity with the wider regeneration benefits considered by the Blue Sky study. A design team completed a

"It isn't a pile of rubbish, it's New Street station!"

(Birmingham Mail)

Masterplan Enhancement Study in April 2004. Consideration was given to the construction of a new station in the Eastside area but this was rejected on cost and accessibility grounds.

In the summer of 2004, the Steering Group reduced in size as a commissioning process was developed for the next stage of the project. Birmingham City Council, Network Rail, the Department for Transport (Rail) (DfT) (former SRA), Centro and AWM determined a series of enduring objectives for the project which aimed to:

- Provide sufficient passenger capacity to meet long term needs
- Improve passenger facilities and the environment within the station
- Installation of ticket barriers
- Improve the overall manageability of the station
- Improve access to, from and in the station for all users
- Improve the interchange capability within the station and between transport modes
- Improve pedestrian access routes to, from and across the city centre
- Transform the appearance of a major civic amenity and it's environs to improve perceptions and stimulate confidence through creating an appropriate gateway to the region
- Improve the urban environment and develop the public realm to catalyse the development and take up of new high quality office space in the city core, resulting in new jobs, and resulting productivity gains
- Create a major private sector commercial development to the southern aspect
- Strategic added value benefits to the city; including initiatives in sustainable development, skills development and training, and information and communication technologies
- Maximise commercial value of the scheme within the passenger capacity and regeneration objectives of the proposal
- Secure the successful re-configuration of the Pallasades Shopping Centre and car park
- Improve access to commercial facilities for all users

The project partners addressed the immediate and long term issues of the station (including the Disability Discrimination Act (1995)), safety concerns resulting from overcrowding and the wider implications for the economy and prosperity of the city, the region, and the national rail network.

Publicity for the project around the 'mousehole' entrance to the station informs users of the upcoming changes.

The project objectives formed part of the terms of reference for a study commissioned by Birmingham City Council in April 2005 for Network Rail to develop design options and consider further options to meet the project objectives. This led to the development of a comprehensive scheme that addressed the station, the Pallasades and surrounding public realm and included a new roof covering over the whole station building and the re-development of Exchange House (Gateway 2). A mid point review led to a revised scheme (Gateway 1) which excluded Exchange House but incorporated an atrium roof over the central core of the Pallasades.

A design report of November 2005 included a draft outline business case and a long list of 18 options to address the project objectives. This was subsequently reduced to a short list of 5 options. These were:

- **Do Minimum** – maintained the existing situation while requiring limited investment, the benchmark for other schemes
- **Incremental** – a rail only option to re-develop the concourse by removing retail provision and increasing gate lines to increase concourse space within the existing area
- **Capacity Masterplan** – a transport only option to remove clutter from the platforms, enlarge existing concourses into the Pallasades Car Park, create a north-south street, a southern plaza and sites for two Southside towers
- **Gateway 2** – as the Capacity Masterplan with a new public square to the east with a retail opportunity, a new wrap façade around the existing building, a fully enclosed wrap roof and redevelopment of Exchange House (the HSBC offices on New Street), an atrium void within the shopping centre to introduce natural light to the concourse and shopping centre, a new north west entrance to the shopping centre and improved vertical links between the concourse and shopping centre
- **Gateway 1** – As Gateway 2, but the wrap roof and Exchange House are excluded

In January 2006 the project stakeholders considered the costs and benefits of each option and resolved unanimously to support Gateway 1 which was deemed to meet all the project objectives and provide the highest value for money.

The full business case and funding package applications were submitted to government in May (Local Transport Plan and AWM) and June 2006 (Network Rail's submission for control period 4). There followed extensive debate with DfT and the Department for Business, Enterprise and Regulatory Reform (DBERR) as they progressed their appraisal of the business case and funding applications.

Following detailed scrutiny and consideration, the DfT requested that the partners develop a new 'lower cost option' in February 2007. This was to include alternative access arrangements, a re-design of the concourse and new access to and from the concourse and platforms. The costs saved were modest (around £33m) and the benefits much reduced (around £600m), and some of the key objectives were not met. In July 2007, the DfT asked that some of the lessons learnt from the development of this lower cost option (including retention of the Navigation Street footbridge, and a more direct eastern access from the Bullring) be applied to the Gateway 1 scheme – producing a variant that became known as Gateway Plus. This increased the public sector cost by around £31m but significantly enhanced the overall benefits (by around £400m) compared to Gateway 1.

A significant advantage of the Gateway Scheme was that it could be phased to keep the station operational throughout the works minimising, as far as possible, disruption and disturbance to the rail network and access to and movement around the city centre.

The approved Gateway Scheme now comprised:

- The removal of 'clutter' from the station platforms, including waiting rooms, smoke lobbies and the former Post Office ramps, to maximise the space available to passengers. Comprehensive refurbishment of the platforms to transform the environment including a new smoke and fume extract system.
- An increase in the number of vertical access connections between the platforms and concourse from

two per platform, to five including the provision of additional escalators and lifts.

- The expansion of the concourse to circa 4.5 times the area of the old concourse. The enlarged concourse to benefit from the introduction of natural daylight as a result of the construction of the new atrium.
- The concourse included a new public north-south street connecting Stephenson Street (north), to Queens Drive (south).
- Within the 'unpaid' area of the concourse a new travel centre (including ticket office), First Class Lounge, Station Control Centre, a Centro Travel Office, and areas of station retail were to be provided.
- Passenger access to the platforms to be through one of two 'paid' concourse areas, with controlled entry into these areas through automated ticket gates.
- New escalators, lifts, and stairs to connect the concourse to the Pallasades to be provided adjacent to the atrium area, with new access to the Pallasades on the north west corner adjacent to Stephenson Street and Lower Temple Street.
- The enlarged concourse to be fully refitted with new floor finishes, ceilings, building services, customer information, and security installations.
- New facilities for taxi pick up and drop off, short stay car parking, public drop off and cycle storage.
- Accommodation for Train Operating Companies and British Transport Police.
- At Pallasades level an atrium to be formed in the centre of the retail area with a new roof to allow natural light to penetrate into the shopping centre and the main areas of the concourse below. This is designed to improve the visual connection between the station and the Pallasades Shopping Centre. The atrium was designed to enhance circulation within the Pallasades by restoring the balance between the east and west malls and achieve a significant improvement in wayfinding through the station and the Pallasades.
- Externally, the station building was to be wrapped in a new façade, and new public realm spaces were to be created between the station and the Bullring, and to the south of the station. The scheme included new 'Southside Steps' connecting the North-South Street to Station Street and Hill Street, and the City beyond. The scheme also created the sites for the construction of two new towers either side of the 'Southside Steps'.

Following the selection of Gateway 1 as the preferred option a planning application was prepared for

Cross-party political support for the project was essential in realising the funding package. Gisela Stuart MP is given a tour of the demolition works by Richard Kirkman and Mick Carter of the project team.

the scheme following an extensive programme of consultation with stakeholders, including statutory bodies, neighbours and interested parties. The Planning Committee meeting of 30th November 2006 resolved to grant consent subject to completion of Section 106 Agreement which was duly completed on 4 July 2007.

The revised Gateway Plus Scheme enhanced the existing access to the east (facing the Bullring) with a connection to the north-south street of Gateway 1. The revised Scheme also included upgraded the Navigation Street Bridge to provide access to all platforms, with widening beyond platforms 8/9. A new southern entrance on Hill Street was included. Customer services facilities including automatic ticket gates and ticket offices were provided on both the existing northern (Navigation Street) end and new southern (Hill Street) end of the bridge. Operational accommodation was relocated off the concourse to facilitate these changes.

The Gateway Plus Scheme was within the outline planning consent.

The Birmingham Gateway Project was identified by government in January 2006 as a number one priority for the West Midlands Region and Birmingham. Funding applications, supported by a high value for money business case in accordance with HM Treasury guidance, were submitted later that year to AWM (£100 million) and DfT (Local Transport Plan (£136 million)) and DfT Rail (£128 million) as part of Network Rail's overall Control Period 4 funding submission.

On 24th July 2007 the DfT announced £128m funding for the project in their High Level Output Specification (HLOS) for the rail industry. AWM Board endorsed funding of £100m which was subsequently approved by DBERR and HM Treasury, and the City Council gained support from the Regional Assembly for an increased Local Transport Plan contribution towards the Gateway Scheme of £160m. Additional local project contributions were agreed with Centro (£10m) and Birmingham City Council (£17m to be secured from developers through Section 106 Agreements).

Following completion of an appraisal and scrutiny process, the government announced approval of the £100m AWM funding and 'Programme Entry' status to a £160m Local Transport Plan (LTP) funding contribution on 12th February 2008. The pivotal announcement was made by Ruth Kelly, the Secretary of State for Transport. This fundamental milestone secured the future of the project and the decision was welcomed by the City Council's Cabinet, who approved the Gateway Plus Scheme as the way forward for the station. The initial funding decisions confirmed the principle of the Gateway Scheme and provided the certainty to progress the next stage of the project. These decisions triggered an intensive 18 month period to complete the scheme design, land assembly process and detailed project and funding agreements.

In March 2008 the Council's Cabinet granted the authority to use Prudential borrowing to acquire the Pallasades on long leasehold interest and facilitate construction of the Gateway Scheme. The Pallasades interest contained essential property, including the Pallasades Shopping Centre and car parks that was required to construct the Gateway scheme. The decision was absolutely critical as without the Pallasades property the Gateway Scheme could not proceed.

At the same time, following a determined period of negotiation a detailed funding agreement was signed with Advantage West Midlands in April 2008. This critical agreement provided early access to funds that were vital to finance the further development of the project.

The decisions made in February, March and April 2008 allowed Birmingham City Council to progress with acquiring the property required to build the Gateway Scheme. The land and property interests at New Street Station and the Pallasades shopping centre were extremely complex having developed over more than 40 years since the station and shopping centre were first opened. In fact, over 500 property interests were identified on multiple levels throughout the existing site. Alongside negotiations with property owners the Council's team prepared one of the largest and most complex compulsory purchase orders in its history. The compulsory purchase order was made in July 2008 which started the statutory process to resolve the land and property ownerships included in the order.

Another key milestone was achieved on 30th October 2008, when the Office of Rail Regulation (ORR) confirmed approval to Network Rail funding of £128m for the Birmingham New Street scheme.

After two years of discussion between the parties a major milestone was reached in January 2009 when a master legal agreement was signed between Birmingham City Council and Network Rail. This key agreement bound the parties together to deliver the Gateway Scheme and confirmed roles and responsibilities. Essentially, the arrangements were for Birmingham City Council to lead on the funding and finance aspects, making them the banker for the project, and Network Rail to lead on the design and construction of the scheme.

The next major milestone was the public inquiry for the compulsory purchase order which was held in February and March 2009. Over 50 objections had been received to the order which needed to be addressed. Following a huge and dedicated effort by the project team negotiated settlements were agreed with a number of objectors. Evidence was presented before the Inspector at the formal proceedings and the remaining objections were heard. Evidence was presented by an array of witnesses in support of the Gateway Scheme. During the inquiry proceedings the project team were able to negotiate settlements with all key objectors culminating on the very last day of the public inquiry with the completion of a major deal by Birmingham City Council to purchase the Pallasades property interests. The Inspector then prepared his report which was duly submitted for consideration. This led to a remarkably rapid confirmation of the compulsory purchase order by the Secretary of State on 30 July 2009.

In August 2009 the detailed funding agreement was signed with Centro securing their £10m contribution to the Gateway Scheme.

A final piece of the funding jigsaw was to finalise the key funding agreement between Birmingham City Council and Department for Transport. Again following a lengthy and complex process, detailed arrangements were successfully agreed for the Department for Transport's £160m contribution towards the Gateway Scheme.

Around the same time the final details of the deal to acquire the Pallasades car park were concluded with NCP to cease operation of the car park.

All the successful progress with funding, land assembly and legal agreements made during 2008 and 2009 enabled agreement between the parties to commence construction works. Work commenced in September 2009, nine months earlier than planned, with the demolition of the lower Pallasades car park to make way for the new western concourse of the Gateway Scheme.

While construction work progressed on the Gateway Scheme, significant effort was made to secure the regeneration of the south side of the station. Following two years of preparatory work by the Council and Network Rail in February 2011, John Lewis announced it was to open a 250,000-square-foot (23,000 m²) department store in Birmingham city centre.

Chris Montgomery (Project Director), Andrew Skidmore (Sponsor) and Mike Whitby (Leader, Birmingham City Council) give Transport Secretary Philip Hammond a tour of the station.

In the latter days of operation New Street was showing its age, presenting a poor first impression for station users.

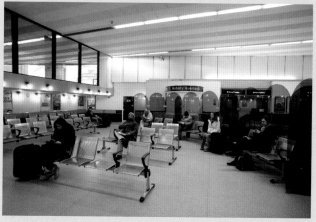

Counting down the final days.

Passenger access to the old station was very limited.

The station was shrouded in 1960s concrete and times and architectural styles have moved on.

At platform level the station was dark, cramped and unwelcoming.

Impressions of the John Lewis store on the south side.

Designing New Street by Carol Stitchman & Alejandro Zaera-Polo

In December 2007, Network Rail in partnership with the RIBA, launched an architectural design competition for the proposed design for Birmingham New Street station and the associated Pallasades shopping centre. The competition brief included the external façade around the perimeter of the building and the internal atrium area. The contest sought to find a visionary concept designer to create a landmark building and create an example of cutting edge architecture.

Six practices were short-listed in February 2008; CRAB Studio, Foreign Office Architects, IDOM UK Ltd, LAB Architecture Studio, UN Studio and Rafael Viñoly Architects.

The winning scheme of Foreign Office Architects was unveiled on 18th September 2008.

Carol Stitchman,
Head of Design

The Design Concept

We recognised that Birmingham New Street station is an important transport hub and a key aspect of the city's public realm. It occupies an important position in the city and handles a large amount of traffic, and it provides the first impression of Birmingham to a large influx of visitors to the Midlands.

Our proposal for Birmingham New Street station sought to produce an iconic architecture that, beyond creating an impression, would be able to communicate to the public, the function of the building and the character of its location at the very centre of Birmingham city. To achieve this I proposed to provide expression to the dynamic nature of the railway theme.

The geometries of motion and the distortion of perception produced by movement have been the inspiration for the architectural expression of the

Alejandro Zaera-Polo,
Partner in Charge
AZPML/FOA

project. The bifurcating, undulating, smooth forms of the track field have been transferred and embedded into the geometry of the building to ornate the city and to convey its historical character as a transportation hub, where various traffic systems – such as the famous canals, the roman roads etc. converge and overlay. The design aimed to trigger a new perception of the urban settings around the station, by specifically reflecting selected areas of the urban landscape around the station.

The design approach aimed to re-establish consistency between form and expression in the new station design, both in the cladding and in the re-organisation of the building. The old structure of the building was built for a different performance to the one that is now being sought, both in organisational and visual terms. As the cladding cannot be used in the interior of the building for practical reasons, the design of the

façade has been related to the exterior space, making the building an instrument to intensify the perception of urban life in Birmingham's inner city, as opposed to try to reveal its inner structure.

This approach is a necessary evolution of the modernist dogmas of transparency towards a more pragmatic and strategic approach necessary to address the complexities of contemporary culture.

By turning the external rain screen into a warping, reflective stainless steel surface, Birmingham New Street Station has been designed to produce controlled reflection of the surrounding urban field to reflect the once dark, now bright Birmingham sky, the crowds of passengers, the trains entering and exiting the station, the hues of the sunset and sunrise, and other dynamic regimes present at the site. To highlight the three main access points, large 'eye-shaped' media screens have been integrated in the façade.

The field of reflections which constitutes the external envelope of the building, and produces a consistent identity, differentiates depending on the opportunities on each side of the building.

Design Co-ordination

Panorama of Bullring entrance at night.

The FOA architectural concept, based upon movement and the reflection of movement, was to inspire the entire project for the design of the platform, concourse and retail areas. The Birmingham Gateway

programme was the largest refurbishment project in Europe at the time and the challenge was to lead, influence and co-ordinate a diverse group of designers to enable the interior design and external landscaping, along with the facade and atrium, to be considered as one holistic design.

The interior design of the concourse enables passengers to engage with the space as a whole and not as individual elements. This immense, open plan space was designed by Atkins to extend uninterrupted views across the area. This breathtaking experience is crowned by the cathedral like quality of the ribbed atrium roof, flooding the interior space with natural daylight. The retail units and lounge areas span across the concourse area and are designed to guide passengers from the main entrances into the central atrium and towards the important focal point of the passenger experience, the ticket office! These spaces are designed with seamless, clear glass that has no projections or sharp corners to empathise with the pure, sinuous lines of the ribbon of stainless steel that forms the external facade.

Inspired by Alejandro Zaera Polo, the floor centre piece is a glass, central lozenge feature, the 'pebble in the pond' with the ripples of granite extending beyond the interior space unifying the external environment. The vast ceiling becomes a wave of open, vertical panels, undulating between the interior spaces with the lighting intent between these panels appearing to 'kiss' the bottom of the wave like sunlight.

A detailed model of the station complex was used to publicise the project.

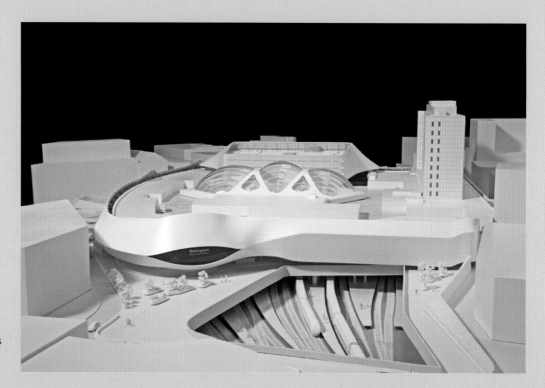

Chris Montgomery (Project Director), explains features of the new station to Transport Secretary Philip Hammond, during a tour of the station.

Opening out the platforms to provide more space,
improve vertical circulation and create a more welcoming
environment was a key feature of the scheme.

The Bullring Square replaces the former cramped and congested station approach.

The Atrium, allowing light to flood down on to the concourse below.

The new food court in Grand Central.

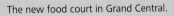

Entrance to John Lewis from Grand Central.

The platform areas offer a much improved vertical circulation and enhanced lighting with the glass centre lozenge offering natural daylight onto the platform area. The wall panelling design gives the same seamless finish as the glazing to the retail units and the stainless steel façade and the open ceiling offer some synergy with the open wavy ceiling in concourse area.

The commercial retail area of the Grand Central Shopping centre is anchored by the John Lewis store. This concept design, again by Alejandro Zaera Polo, offers a curved, crystal like form of fritted, structural glass to give a shimmering effect in the sunlight. At night, this façade becomes a translucent glimpse into the busy retail environment. The interior of the shopping centre, designed by Haskolls, offers the same open plan design as the concourse space with a gentle, plasterboard rippling ceiling.

The external landscaping was designed with an echo of movement identified by the choice of plant species, changing with the seasons. Granite panels cladding the large, eastern parapet walls offer the same seamless design as the façade, and the introduction of a new glass parapet wall allows passengers a view into the operational railway experiencing the direct movement of trains or a reflective, distorted view of movement from the façade.

Throughout the design and delivery, the concept design has not been diluted as can often happen when an inspirational design becomes a reality of the built form. The concept has changed little from the competition entry and has been strengthened by the interior design which complements the contemporary atrium roof. This has generated an inspirational building with a clear legible, external presence which will become an integral part of the fabric of the city of Birmingham.

New Street Station
Client: Network Rail Ltd.
Concept architect: AZPML
Facade structure engineer: AKTII
M&E engineer (Grand Central): Hoare Lea
Project construction management (Delivery Partner): Mace
Executive architect (Lead Consultant): Atkins
Structural engineer: Atkins
M&E engineer: Atkins
QS(Cost Consultant): Faithful & Gould
John Lewis Int. Architect (Grand Central Lead Designer): Haskoll

AZPML/FOA Team credits:
AZPML/FOA Partner-in-Charge: Alejandro Zaera-Polo with:
Manuel Eijo, Guillermo Fernandez-Abascal, Charles Valla, Christof Trenner, Tommaso Franzolini, Lola Fernandez, Sukyeong Kim, Carmen Sagredo, Takeru Sato, Penny Sperbund, Niklavs Paegle, Tobias Jewson, Mio Sato, Manuel Távora

CGIs and Construction progress photo credits:
Network Rail and AZPML

The station enjoys new entrances to the north and south, improving accessibility across the city and honouring the obligation to allow access across the station site.

The final piece of ETFE is added to the atrium roof, September 2014.

Mace: Delivering the project by Martyn Woodhouse

Creating a partnership

To achieve a refurbishment of this magnitude, Network Rail decided to adopt a structure for delivering the works that it had never used before. Instead of the conventional 'fixed price' contract, Network Rail opted to appoint a delivery partner to work as part of an integrated team with its own staff, representing a departure from traditional forms of procurement.

The model is very similar to the relationship between the Olympic Delivery Authority and its partner CLM – a joint venture between CH2M Hill, Laing O'Rourke and Mace – to deliver the 2012 Olympic and Paralympic Games. In August 2008 Network Rail appointed one of those partners, Mace, to be its partner for the scheme. We have been delighted to be involved ever since, with Atkins appointed as executive architect, structural engineer and M&E engineer.

The approach is based on the construction management model in which Mace and Network Rail procure the packages

Martyn Woodhouse, Project Director, Mace

direct from suppliers. It helped us to create a structure where we accessed the expertise from specialist contractors and worked as a joint team to tackle each of the challenges we faced across the project.

As delivery partner we coordinated the individual packages, managed their implementation on site and ensured that the different projects added up to a programme that delivers. We also made sure they were safe, which has been one of the most critical objectives for the scheme as a whole, and one for which I'd personally like to commend everyone involved.

This was a fantastic project for us from the outset. Birmingham New Street is one of the UK's highest profile construction schemes, and has been a unique opportunity for us to tackle a landmark project with a client that wanted to push the boundaries for better project delivery.

Keeping New Street moving

With 170,000 passengers per day and trains arriving or departing every 37 seconds, Birmingham New Street station is a complex operation – even before you add in four Train Operating Companies, a shopping centre and a home for 1,500 rail staff. It is even more complex as a construction site.

In planning the project, our challenge was to devise a schedule that would allow people to use the station – continuously and without disruption – in the course of £750 million of construction work.

The answer came from an unlikely source: a multi-storey car park to the west of the existing cramped concourse. Network Rail purchased the structure at the beginning of the project and we created a phased strategy that would see us spending the first half of the programme creating a new concourse from that car park.

Our plan was to switch passengers to the new concourse at the midway point of the project and close off the east half of the station so the old concourse, and the Pallasades above, could be transformed into the amazing space you can see today.

This chapter looks at how the redevelopment came together – its key milestones, and the companies that made the project possible. But all of these projects are defined by their context: the sheer proximity to the public every step of the way, the need to keep New Street moving and the huge logistical challenges that the site poses – not to mention the complexity and variety of the type of work we had going on at any one moment in time.

New Street was originally built in the 1850s and redeveloped into its tight, concrete-heavy environment in the 1960s. We had scant drawings for either, meaning we have constantly had to deal with uncharted territory. It is classed as a sub-surface station, too, meaning it's more akin to working on an underground station, including strict conditions for managing the risk of a fire.

Despite the scale of the redevelopment, we were working on a very constrained site in the middle of an incredibly busy city centre. Logistics have been challenging and we have had to contend with a lack of space for storing and delivering materials, not to mention removing the tens of thousands of tonnes of concrete that have been taken from the site over six years of demolition and construction.

Within this environment, the redevelopment has encompassed a phenomenal range of engineering and construction feats to achieve the transformational vision set out by the funding partners – all with the ambition of creating a landmark for Birmingham and enabling growth across the city.

But at its core this has been a railway station and shopping centre first, and a construction site second. Behind the scenes our workforce peaked at over 3,000 people on site. Our project office averaged around 130 – creating the strategies, techniques and plans to make this transformation possible. Innovation and a willingness to use different approaches have been essential. And our programme has been focused entirely on delivering these works safely and efficiently, while minimising the impact on the station and its passengers.

Phase One

First: remove one car park

Having been established in 1962 just two and a half miles from Birmingham New Street, by 2009 Coleman & Company had become a renowned demolition specialist. We appointed them as our contractor for the demolition of the NCP car park that would form the new western concourse. The project laid the foundation for a relationship with Coleman & Company that would see them on site for six continuous years throughout the project.

The car park sat directly on top of the railway lines (separated by just a few feet of concrete) and immediately beneath the Pallasades shopping centre. In total, we had to remove 8,000 tonnes of concrete from that space, including an entire mezzanine floor above the first level of the car park, to double the height of the new concourse's ceiling.

The bottom floor of the car park gave us a base to work from, but could not support the weight of the sections of concrete we were removing from the mezzanine slab above. Nor could we use anything for the demolition that would cause additional noise, vibration or dust for the rest of the station and the nearby area.

We developed a "track and hover" system that would support the weight of the beams as they were cut, and slide them out of the car park on crane rails that ran the length of the building. We used this format for the entire mezzanine slab and two floors of the adjacent Pallasades shopping centre.

Work started in September 2009. The process lasted 65 weeks with 60 operatives at peak moving blocks weighing up to ten tonnes – all while leaving passengers unaffected. Coleman & Company won World Demolition Contractor of the Year in November 2011 following completion of the works, and over 90 per cent of the material was re-used.

Changes in plan

Six months after we started on site, John Lewis was announced as the anchor for the redevelopment's commercial element. It was terrific news for the scheme and helped to build excitement for everything we were delivering. But it meant a major alteration to the original plans for the 'hinterland' to the south of the station too and, for the project team, it meant a major redesign of the job.

This had a knock-on effect for the construction programme, and our challenge was to complete it in the same timescales despite the redesign. Primarily it brought forward our work to clear the hinterland in preparation for the redevelopment, and meant we focused a huge amount of effort into moving items like primary incoming services and switchboxes to make the construction and logistics possible.

Installing services – taking it off-site

One of the key milestones in creating the new concourse was to replace the equipment providing electrical and mechanical services to the station and all of the platforms. Dubbed the 'engine room', the existing unit ran down the wall between the old east concourse and the new west section. It was outdated and contained asbestos, and had to be replaced as part of the refurbishment to create space for the new atrium.

The plan had originally been to thread new services throughout the building, but we worked with M&E specialist NG Bailey to develop a better approach.

We decided on a system that would install a single service 'spine' consisting of 24 modules, built off-site and installed to form a single unit along the width of the station. It's a colossal structure. The 300 tonne spine includes two maintenance walkways and suspended plant rooms, as well as external cladding for fire protection. It measures seven metres wide, three metres high and spans 126 metres across New Street: all designed to provide essential power and services to keep the station functioning.

NG Bailey manufactured the spine's modules at its own facility. They then installed the 24 modules in just 15 working days. All the work was carried out by a team of eight, working between 8pm and 7am. Delivery was meticulously planned from the outset, both through 4D modelling and with a factory prototype.

The system saved 10,000 working hours by moving most of the work to the factory floor, and reduced carbon emissions by 57 per cent through lower amounts of waste. This was NG Bailey's biggest ever example of manufacturing a services system off-site. It was delivered ahead of schedule and now has a life span of some 60 years.

Transforming the platforms

Part of the project's vision has been to create more accessible, brighter and clearer platforms, with new escalators and lifts to the redeveloped concourse.

We reviewed the station's operations with Network Rail and found that the station could operate with one platform shut at a time without reducing the volume of arrivals and departures. The platform works included new surfaces, drainage and services, as well as the improved vertical access from the lifts and escalators.

We made significant savings on the platforms' ventilation: removing the need for any ductwork by using impulse fans that run above the length of the platform – taking in clean air at one end, and pushing it out at the other. The design also reduced the number of risers through the building, which created additional concourse and retail space.

To overcome the logistical challenges of getting materials to the platforms, we made deliveries for the refurbishment by rail and used sidings at Bordesley as an impromptu depot.

We went through a "station change" process with each of the train operating companies (TOCs) for the parts of the programme that affected them. This involved setting out what the changes were, what impact they would have on the TOCs' operations, and providing financial indemnity if anything provided further disruption to their services.

Our first platform took 26 weeks to deliver but, after reviewing the programme, we reduced this to just 12 weeks for each of the remaining platforms.

Working through Christmas

Phase One also included opening the new entrance on Hill Street at the south side of the station, by extending the Navigation Street footbridge. The bridge previously had only one exit (onto Navigation Street) and only served platforms 2 to 11, meaning a long walk round for passengers using platforms 1 and 12.

Our challenge was to extend the bridge without disruption to the tens of thousands of passengers using it each day. We couldn't do it safely or without taking away access to the platforms while services were running. Instead, we planned to extend the footbridge over the Christmas break while the rail network was closed.

It had originally been planned for Christmas 2010, and would see our contractor, Volker Fitzpatrick, move a 700 tonne crane close enough to the station to safely remove the existing narrow bridge span which served platforms 10 and 11. The crane would then lift the new section into place.

The weather had other ideas. December 2010 saw the 'Big Freeze' with temperatures hitting -10°C, and heavy snow forcing closures and disruptions at the UK's airports and across the rail network. While this thwarted our plans for December 2010, we regrouped for 2011 and used the break in services between Christmas Eve and Boxing Day to complete the operation.

The wider 2011 Christmas programme allowed us to hit a number of key milestones by taking advantage of the absence of passengers. During this time we managed the works to erect a tower crane outside the front of the station, which would be used to build the new public square, and we removed the old Pallasdes link bridge and the escalator above Station Street.

Transforming the south side

In the same period work continued at a pace on the 'hinterland' at the south side of the station. The original plan for the site was for two towers – both with retail, commercial office space and residential units – to replace the 200 foot Stephenson Tower which had been built as part of the 1960s redevelopment.

However, the John Lewis building is an extension of the main station building, rather than the two

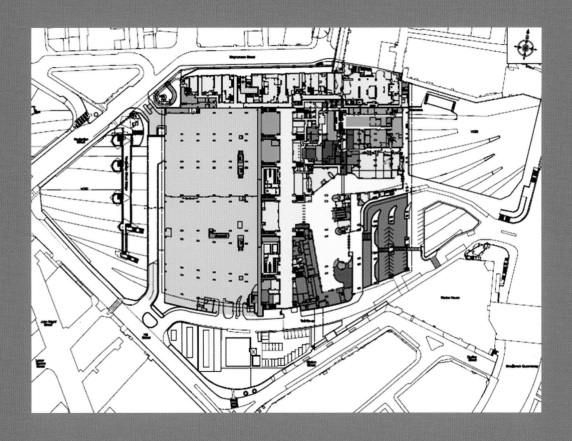

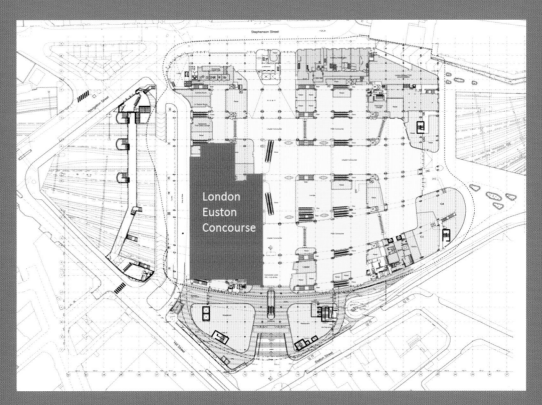

Before and after at concourse level: almost half of the original concourse level (top) was taken up by the car park, with a very limited area available for passenger circulation. The delivery team exploited this fact to build the first part of the new station in this area, allowing the old concourse to continue in operation unchanged until the 'half time switchover'. The extension of the concourse area and the addition of the Bullring square is evident in the finished station plan (left), with an outline of the area of London Euston concourse shown for comparison.

Transforming the South Side – the demolition of Stephenson Tower

separate structures originally proposed, requiring Atkins to embark on a major redesign.

Stephenson Tower had to be demolished under either scenario, so that was a part of the programme that could be delivered while Atkins were revising plans elsewhere. The tower was incredibly close to the station and particularly to platform 12, so it couldn't be taken down by controlled explosion. Instead, the tower was removed layer by layer and transported back through the structure – effectively folding the tower in on itself.

We appointed Keltbray for the demolition in late 2010 and, by January 2011, we had installed a 500-tonne crane and encapsulated the building in scaffolding to allow the demolition to start. While the project applied for and secured planning permission for the John Lewis building (which was granted in May 2011), we prepared the tower for demolition and, in June, started the careful process of removing around 10,000 tonnes of materials.

The tower was completely removed by February 2012, paving the way for the landmark John Lewis store. We broke ground for the new John Lewis building in late June 2012, with David Higgins, then-Network Rail's CEO, Andy Street, Managing Director of John Lewis, Mike Whitby, then leader of Birmingham City Council, and Mark Reynolds, Mace's then-Deputy CEO on site to celebrate the milestone.

Sustainability and the Lamp Block building

Passengers were not the only people using the station every day; so our work was carefully planned to have as little impact on the retailers, train operating companies and their 1,500 staff.

One of the largest operators at New Street is CrossCountry Trains. All of their trains pass through the station and 400 of its staff are based here. Between 2011 and 2012, we built a state of the art new commercial office for its staff, and did so to exacting sustainability standards.

The new building, called the Lamp Block, sits on the site of a 19th century gas lamp depot that gave the office its name. It is situated between a sheer rock face and the live railway line.

The Lamp Block was created from 57 steel-framed modules that were built off-site. The manufacturer, Caledonian Modular, finished the interiors as far as possible in the factory to take working hours away

Demolition of
Stephenson Tower.

The completed Lamp Block building on platform 1 – a new home for CrossCountry Trains.

71

The Moor Street Link opened up inter-station connectivity and helped establish the project's sustainability credentials with the addition of a Green Wall.

from the site. The complete building features locker rooms for changing in and out of uniforms, office space, meeting rooms and a staff dining area. It's a fully-functioning modern office covering 1,268 square metres of space.

On completion, the Lamp Block building became the railway network's first BREEAM Excellent building – with no other structures at stations or within a live rail environment having achieved the standard at that time. It includes photo voltaic panels, a solar thermal system for heating water, and a green roof containing over 14 different species of plant. The Lamp Block opened as the new home to CrossCountry's workforce in June 2012, a year after work on the design and planning began.

Ready for changeover

We discovered major issues with the existing concrete structure in late 2011, which had a significant knock-on effect for installing the escalators and fitting out the new concourse. The second multi-storey car park (at the upper western edge of the station) had to be completely replaced, rather than refurbished, because the concrete slabs had been severely corroded by de-icing salts. Demolishing and replacing the structure was the most cost effective option.

The concrete in an area designated for new offices for Network Rail had become damaged by chlorides in an effect known as "concrete cancer" by the team. We demolished the beams and areas of the slabs that had been affected – doubling the scale of the work. We kept it on track by switching to 24/7 working to absorb nine months of additional work into the original nine month schedule.

While construction continued to create the new concourse in 2012, we hit a succession of milestones that were particularly visible to the public. The Pallasades car park closed for demolition in May 2012 and construction began on the Moor Street Link – the now-familiar route running behind the Odeon, through the station and onto Stephenson Street. The elevated walkway was delivered by Balfour Beatty – its first contract at the station.

We also started work on the new entrance at the corner of Stephenson Street and Navigation Street. The entrance includes the distinctive 'Eye', which has become an icon of the redevelopment.

Making the switch

The first phase of the project culminated with the transition to the new west concourse, created in the space that had previously been occupied by the NCP car park. The changeover earned the nickname of the 'Half Time Switchover' but, once again, the existing structure put significant barriers in our path. In the six months leading up to the switchover, we discovered further concrete decay on the upper mezzanine level, and had to demolish the concrete slab and beams, rebuilding them as we moved forward.

The final stages of 'Phase One' included the fit out of the new concourse and its retail units, and the construction of modularised pedestrian tunnels that would allow passengers to move from the new concourse to the pre-existing escalators, through the sections of the site that were to be closed off for construction.

We put in 250,000 working hours in April 2013 alone, and had 1,300 people on site per day at the peak: all working behind the scenes from the public to make the Half Time Switchover a reality.

The changeover took place on Sunday 28 April 2013 and was manned by over 200 local volunteers to guide passengers and staff through the new areas and their links to the platforms below, to help people adjust to the new environment, and understand any teething issues. Representatives from organisations such as RNIB, Deaf UK and Age UK were involved to make sure everyone was catered for.

On the other side of the hoardings, our teams had spent the past week commissioning and testing all the station's life safety systems. Due to the structural issues during the fit out works phases, the systems were eventually completed a week beforehand, leaving a week to commission, test and witness the installations and complete a series of critical cause and effect trails to prove the systems were fully integrated. The team worked relentlessly to achieve this tough assignment successfully.

A reflection of Birmingham: creating the iconic façades

One of the redevelopment's most striking features is its façade. The stainless steel creates a mirror image of Birmingham, the train tracks and the sky, and was described by *Building* magazine during construction as 'instantly iconic'.

It's a part of the programme that has spanned both phases of the redevelopment, and has been a huge undertaking because of the scale and complexity of the installation. The façade covers 16,000m² around the station. It is formed of more than 5,000 panels, more than two thirds of which are unique in size.

The panels are fixed to a steel frame that creates the curved exterior by angling the panels. The frame is attached to the main building structure, and we carried out detailed analysis of the concrete's condition to assess where the frame could be attached. It is part of the programme that has particularly benefitted from 4D modelling due to the variety and intricacy of the installation.

The façade's first major milestone came in March 2010, when Network Rail unveiled a 'mock-up' of its proposed design at Bordesley. This not only revealed the design vision, but was also a vital part of our planning. The mock-up allowed the team to trial different materials and fixings so they could settle on a practical and workable design that would become a defining part of the project.

The installation was carried out by specialist contractor Martifer. AKTII was responsible for the structural design of the façade, and they worked closely with Atkins to develop the approach. Martifer began installing the façade on the north side of the station in 2012, including the new entrance onto New Street. Following the north side, the team moved to the north-west section, before finishing with the more complex east and south sides.

After extensive research, the panels have been carefully arranged to avoid reflecting sunlight at train drivers, or obscure signalling.

Health and safety

From the outset, we developed a joint vision for health and safety that has brought the whole site together. As one of our first projects with Network Rail, we worked quickly to align both of our safety cultures and practices.

This led to the creation of a common set of health and safety house rules for contractors, employees, operatives and stakeholders working on or visiting the site, incorporating Mace's health and safety culture and policy "Safety first. Second nature".

We engaged with the whole workforce to achieve the right level of buy-in to our initiatives, and recognised the various language and communications requirements of everyone on site – in some instances running sessions in up to five languages. Safety leadership meetings and quarterly safety forums have been pivotal in ensuring we successfully embedded a collaborative approach to safety. Our safety managers also embraced the influence of data: generating high levels of feedback through our reporting system – Yellow Jacket – that allowed them to pick out and address trends.

Not only have we targeted exceptional safety standards, but we looked closely at the health requirements of our workforce. We had a dedicated site nurse, blood pressure testing and campaigns key health issues, in addition to helping reduce the number of smokers in our workforce, raise awareness about alcohol abuse and improve the diet of the people working here.

BIM and lean construction

The project has capitalised on Building Information Modelling (BIM). BIM is used to create digital models of buildings that we can then use to plan and manage construction works.

We used BIM from the earliest stages of the project to map out every step of the works – visualising all the sequences before they took place. It helped us to model and trial different approaches to the site's challenges, so we could optimise and accomplish individual tasks.

It gave us tangible benefits. Initially, the delivery schedule for the atrium demolition was 12 months.

Raising the roof

View of the emerging atrium from Ladywood House. The John Lewis structure is complete and the background and the new car park rises alongside.

The mesh of steelwork to form the atrium takes shape, with the roof being used as a base for construction prior to demolition.

Raising the roof

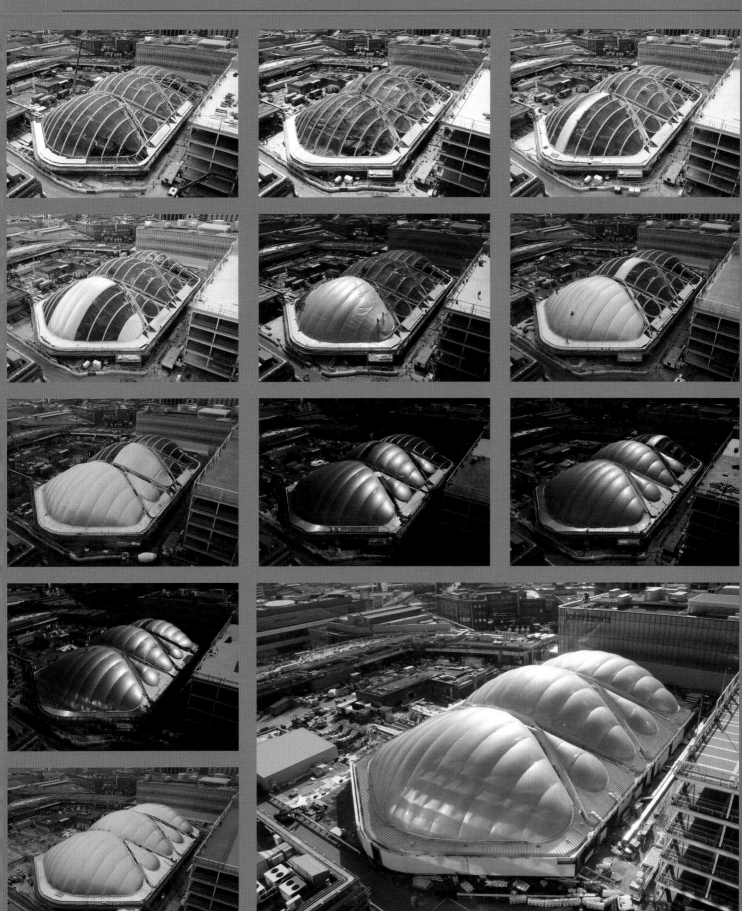

The tunnel move

Moving the passenger walkway 'tunnel' to allow construction work to continue (top). The giant jaws of Coleman's innovative 'muncher' (bottom) made light work of concrete removal.

The visit of Prime Minister David Cameron and Chancellor George Osborne in September 2014 was a project highlight during the atrium demolition works.

Carving out the atrium

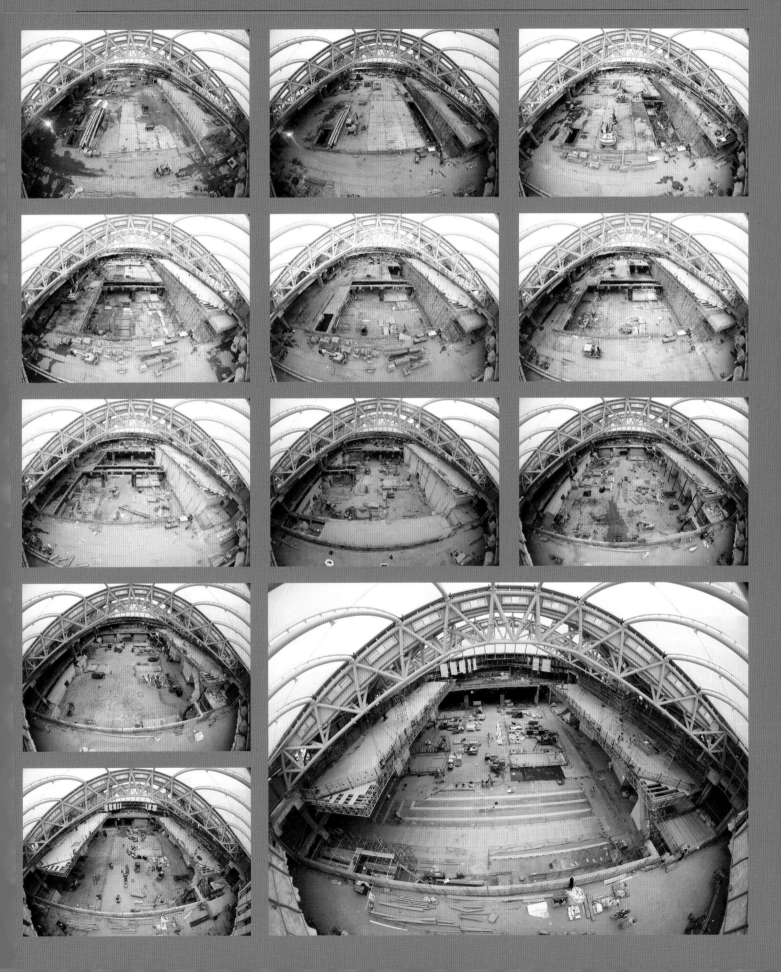

Building the Eastern Facade

Getting ready for the half time switchover

By looking at different approaches we reduced it to six. We refined the tunnel move project from two weeks to a 57-hour window over a bank holiday weekend.

BIM has also helped to bring new skills onto site. Members of our team now have software design experience – rather than purely a construction background – and it's helped us to build more efficiently.

Towards completion, we used the model to help familiarise occupiers and passengers with the station. We even created a version of the model with video game graphics so that our stakeholders could experience what it would be like to walk around the station in a way that simple site visits have never been able to replicate.

Phase Two

Stripping out the old concourse

With Phase One's new concourse open to the public, Phase Two began in May 2013 with the soft strip demolition of the old east concourse, which was complicated by large quantities of asbestos covering the concourse's services.

The lack and inaccuracy of 'as built' drawings for live services and internal structures required a comprehensive programme of surveys to be commissioned. But access to asbestos surveys was limited by difficulties in gaining access to the concourse, resulting in a much more iterative process.

We developed a comprehensive asbestos management plan, which ultimately led to the project committing over 60,000 hours to the removal of asbestos prior to the start of demolition activities.

With this new knowledge, the team had to slowly progress hand demolition activities in line with the physical tracing of services before progressing to more economical means of demolition.

Raising the roof

This painstaking preparatory work and demolition allowed us to begin on some of the signature parts of the station in Phase Two. The atrium roof is perhaps one of the most striking architectural features of the new station. The dramatic new tubular steel frame is covered with a lightweight and self-cleaning ETFE (ethylene tetrafluoroethylene) roof covering that allows light to flood the concourse. The material was also used on the Eden Project in Cornwall, the outside of Bayern Munich's Allianz Arena, and the Beijing National Aquatics Centre.

A key part of the project was to transfer the weight of the new roof to the structure beneath. The new roof design consists of two elongated domes with wishbone-shaped spines, that carry the loads to a steel box girder perimeter beam. This, in turn, transfers the loads to the existing concrete frame, enabling the slab inside the perimeter beam to be cut out to create the first level of atrium space.

The reality of the load transfer was far from simple. We created a two-stage process that saw the steelwork erected on temporary trestles, and welded up. The temporary works were then taken away – completing the first stage. The second stage was to cut the beam below and jack the remaining structure into the perimeter box girder, which now took the load of the roof above, and the two small sections of the original concrete roof slab that have now been retained.

Managing the whole structure's global stability has been a constant challenge. Not only does the new roof change the load profile, but the John Lewis store also significantly changes the way load is distributed and the temporary work has meant that the core structure was in a constant state of flux throughout the build. The façade effectively hangs off the side of the building, which was a further consideration, and Atkins specifically managed these challenges throughout the scheme using a global stability analysis model and construction sequence analysis.

In the case of the roof, the steelwork was originally constructed off the old roof meaning that, for a period of time, the load to the structure below was significantly higher. We had to temporarily strengthen the columns beneath the old roof to take the weight of both structures, until we could demolish the old concrete slab.

Once the load transfer was complete in June 2014, July saw the first pieces of ETFE attached to the atrium roof, a significant milestone for the programme.

Bank Holiday tunnel move

The load transfer was critical to the programme as it allowed the team to start demolishing the supporting concrete below the roof to form the atrium. However, another enabling factor for the atrium demolition was to relocate a passenger tunnel that lay beneath the demolition area.

Although the concourses had been switched over in April 2013, we couldn't move the stairs and escalators to the platforms until later in the programme. So a tunnel was installed to take passengers safely through the newly-closed off construction site to the pre-existing stairs and escalators for the platforms.

We knew in advance that we would need to re-route the tunnel halfway through Phase Two to allow demolition to continue above, and to access new stairs and escalators to the trains.

Our response was to develop a modular tunnel that could be built quickly, installed efficiently and, crucially, be redirected without causing disruption. After a two week off-site build, the tunnel was installed for the opening of Phase One, with prefabricated sections coming in at night. A 'plug and play' system for the tunnel's M&E was a key part of the design. It allowed us to quickly provide power and other services to the modules, meaning we could detach the services just as easily when it came to moving the tunnel.

We planned meticulously – with extensive 4D modelling – so that moving the tunnel, which took half the station's traffic to the platforms, would impact the travelling public as little as possible. It took ten months to refine the plans and secure our stakeholder's confidence in our proposals to cut the programme down from two weeks to just 57 hours – short enough to be executed over the UK August Bank Holiday weekend. We shut the tunnel to the travelling public on the Saturday evening, and opened the new route up for the first trains at 05:00 after the Bank Holiday on Tuesday morning.

Carving out the atrium

With the roof level load transfer successfully completed in June 2014, followed by the tunnel move in August, Coleman & Company started on the demolition of the floors beneath to create the impressive atrium.

Specialist machinery, combined with thorough planning and BIM modelling, helped us to develop an approach that would allow work to continue through the night without disrupting people nearby. This was critical and helped us to reduce the atrium programme from twelve months to just six.

The specially commissioned 'Mega Muncher' JCB excavator, which is remote controlled with a bespoke cracker attachment, pulverised the concrete beams instead of breaking them. Some of the removed beams weighed more than the equivalent of 30 Range Rovers. The excavator therefore minimised noise and enabled the team to work on site 24 hours a day, 7 days a week.

Remote controlled Brokks were also used to remove the floor slabs and to break up the concrete slabs once they had been taken down. Acoustic screens minimised the noise reaching the station's neighbours and constant noise monitoring took place around the site.

Removing such a large amount of concrete from the centre of the building within a live station environment was a huge feat of engineering, which finally saw completion in February 2015 with the momentous removal of the final concrete layer underneath the new roof.

Early access for John Lewis

On the south side of the station, Phase Two saw the completion of the new John Lewis store. At 23,000 square metres it is one of the retailer's largest stores outside of London.

We were asked to provide 'early access' from 5 November 2014 to enable John Lewis to commence early fit out works including escalators, roof plant and lift installation. To do this, we worked closely with John Lewis to bring in their 'early access' elements much more quickly than originally planned. This included facilitating access for the escalator about 12 months early whilst the tower cranes were in place and the escalators could be delivered through a convenient gap in the roof finishes.

Ahead of the building's practical completion, we achieved a number of significant milestones including successfully passing the BSRIA air test and are on target to securing BREEAM 'Excellent'. While the fit out began, Mace continued its responsibility for health and safety practices within the whole project until final handover, with over 1,500 operatives on site at any one time 24 hours a day.

Successful handover to the client for fit-out reached practical completion in January 2015 and marked another timely key deliverable in the project journey.

Fitting out Grand Central

As the fit out phase got underway in Grand Central, the logistics of managing 60 retailers and their contractors had to be meticulously planned and co-ordinated. It marked the peak number of workers on site, and the first step was to open the main delivery access ramp up on roof level. The roof was being clad at the same time, so we organised "access windows" to manage restricted times for deliveries.

Retention of the tunnels permitting public access across the site meant that constraints around the lower retail works had to be controlled. When the mall works opened to the public in May 2015 this enabled us to remove the tunnel that dissected the eastern retail units, allowing for completion of works in these units in June 2015. This completion date coincided with the retail tenant contractors commencing their fit out works.

All the incoming extra retail construction contractors meant the site had to 'ramp up' to accommodate a total of circa 3,000 construction staff at its peak period, up from the original daily 1,000.

An 'Entry into Service' steering group was formed to cover the process of interfacing between Birmingham City Council and its agents and allowing all parties in the retail handover process time to align their completions with the landlord.

Grand Central construction was complicated by the need to work around live retail tenants including The Perfume Shop and Footlocker, located in the north east corner of the station. The fit out of John Lewis took place at the same time, along with other external works programmes and the closing of Station Street, a busy road outside the site.

New Street: New Start

The final stage of the programme was to prepare the new concourse and link it to the existing station. In addition to Grand Central, the new concourse has 25 retail units, ticket gates, toilets and new facilities and accommodation for London Midland traincrew – all of which were fitted out in the run up to opening.

The final works also included the ceiling, floors and wall finishes and – as with Phase One – integrating the services into the new concourse and testing and commissioning them for public use. We completed the vertical access to Grand Central and the platforms and, finally, created the link between the east and west concourses – joining together the team's achievements from both phases under the new roof.

This has been an historic construction project for Mace, Network Rail and all of our partners. It really has been a collaborative effort and I'd like to say thank you again to all of our colleagues, our partners in Network Rail, Atkins and throughout the supply chain for making this an exceptional project to be a part of.

The construction programme has generated careers, innovation, improved the health of its workforce and brought together dozens and dozens of companies. In addition to the technical feats that we have achieved together throughout the scheme, we'd also like to put on record how proud we are that this scheme will deliver amazing results for Birmingham. We fully believe this will be a landmark project for the city, and living proof that transport can transform cities.

Adding the Façade

The first completed area of façade was in Stephenson Street, creating an immediate impact.

The façade was fixed to a steel frame, enveloping the original structure.

Stripping the old concourse

Work began to strip away familiar features of the old concourse after the 'half time switchover'.

Adding a John Lewis store

The addition of a John Lewis store on the south side was confirmed after project work had begun. The framework steel of the building is evident, as the distinctive fritted glass panels are fixed to the exterior.

The use of large cranes during construction necessitated road closures and considerable support from the City Council and local neighbours. A tidy worksite was a notable feature of the construction period. The design concept was very closely delivered by the project team – the John Lewis store will be a city landmark by day or night (opposite).

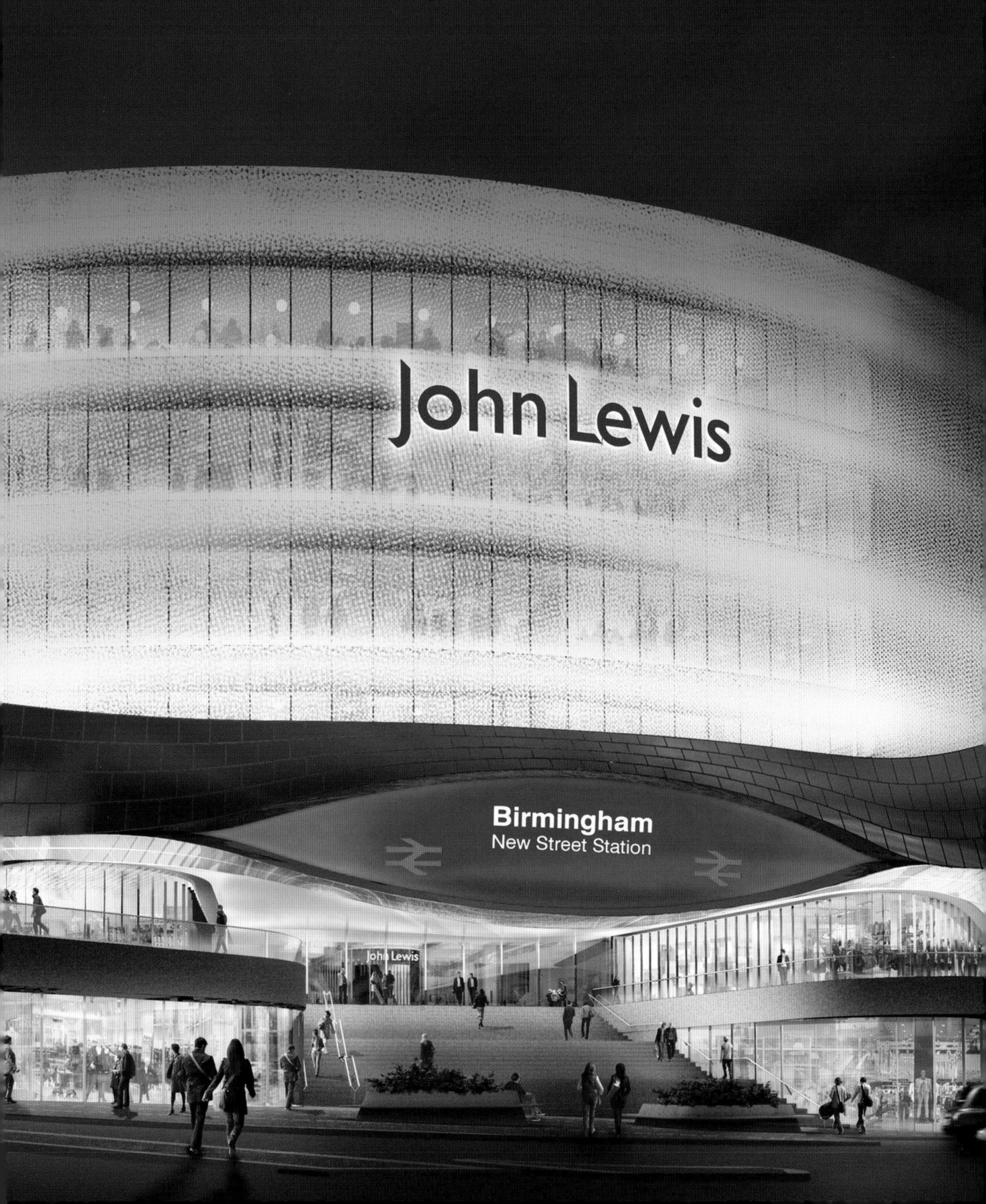
John Lewis
Birmingham
New Street Station
John Lewis

Views from the Network Rail helicopter

Bullring entrance

Taxi turning circle and south side entrance

Moor Street Link and Bullring square

Façade steelwork linking John Lewis and the car park

Navigation Street bridge

Western façade steelwork

Car park and John Lewis

Station roof and John Lewis

Bullring square

The atrium and car park

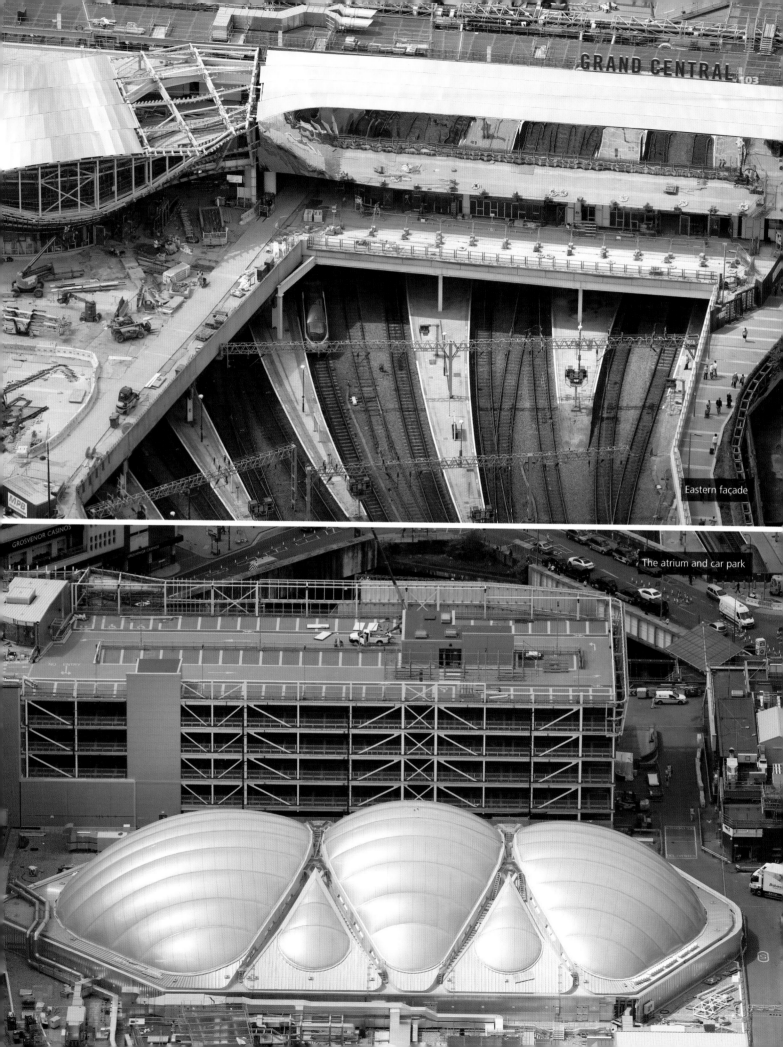

Eastern façade

The atrium and car park

Azhar Quaiyoom, Engineering Programme Manager

Sustainability
by Azhar Quaiyoom

The architectural challenge for the project was how to turn Birmingham New Street station from a dark, unwelcoming and overcrowded hub with poor access for passengers, into a light bright welcoming space. Alongside this, the environmental challenge was to convert a very dated, poorly controlled and energy intensive heating, cooling and ventilation system into a modern, green, sustainable development while adhering to stringent rail standards.

When the project commenced design in 2008, Network Rail was in its infancy regarding corporate policy and guidelines for creating sustainable transport hubs and the BREEAM methodology. So when the funding partners set the goal of achieving a BREEAM minimum rating of 'Very Good', the team knew that this would not be a straightforward target to achieve against a background of complex refurbishment in a rail environment.

Network Rail and delivery partner Mace, backed by Birmingham City Council, Centro and the DfT, needed to deliver the kind of station passengers deserve: one that the people of Birmingham could be really proud of with sustainability credentials not previously achieved for a major railway station of this kind.

The first part of the new station opened to the public in April 2013 and provided a fantastic experience for everyone who passed through its doors, being brighter and lighter than before and giving a much improved first impression of the city. By 2015, 36 new escalators and 15 new lifts had been installed - reaching every platform. The exterior of the station is clad in a stunning new stainless steel façade and the construction of the huge atrium allows natural light to flood into the station concourse.

However, complying with current legislation for disabled access for a sub-surface station with additional lifts, escalators and increased concourse capacity and retail facilities, also significantly increases energy requirements. Therefore it was very important that, with such an increase in energy consumption, options for low or zero carbon solutions should be explored to satisfy the triple bottom line for a sound economic, environmental and social case, as well as a safe one for the daily users of the station.

Refurbishing a 1960s structure to meet modern day sustainability requirements in a busy city centre brought challenges, however the project team worked hard to gain green credentials for the project through recycling and energy monitoring initiatives as well as working closely with the designers and regulatory bodies.

The completed station now incorporates:
- Low energy and high efficiency LED lighting
- 60% of toilet flushing demand provided by rainwater harvesting system
- Efficient water spray taps for water conservation
- Energy efficient lifts and escalators
- Sub-metering for all water, heating and cooling to monitor energy consumption
- Natural daylight for the concourse and natural ventilation where possible to minimise energy consumption
- Responsibly and legally sourced materials including timber
- Use of alternative materials such as carpet tiles containing yarn made from recycled fishing nets

Birmingham New Street is Network Rail's first station to incorporate a stand alone Combined Heat and Power (CHP) plant with the station electricity taken from the plant and waste heat transferred into a city centre district heating scheme.

Waste recycling

Over 7,500 tones of concrete was removed from the former Pallasades car park on the west side of the old station to create space for the first phase station concourse that opened in April 2013. Waste concrete removed from this site was taken to a waste recycling facility for use on other projects. 98% of the material from the demolished Stephenson Tower (now the site of the John Lewis department store) was also recycled.

The project met its aim to recycle/re-use a minimum of 95% of the non-hazardous waste material, and this was exceeded in elements of the demolition works and general waste. We engaged closely with our supply chain in respect of waste and our main waste contractor, Weir Waste, used a new local state of the art facility to segregate and recycle construction waste.

Energy Monitoring

The redevelopment project also installed a sub-metering system to permit accurate measurement of water, electricity and carbon usage across the worksite on a daily basis. This helped the project to monitor targets and reduce consumption throughout the works, with the information shared around the works site and canteen areas.

BREEAM

BREEAM has become the principle measure used to describe a building's environmental performance and Network Rail is dedicated to ensuring best practice for sustainability measures wherever possible.

It has been a tough journey but the station met its target to gain a BREEAM rating of 'very good' for the design stage. The project team monitored construction activity to ensure this rating was maintained throughout the build and in the finished station.

Procurement and Site Management

Network Rail and its partners worked closely with external bodies throughout the project, including The Carbon Trust, WRAP (Waste & Resource Action Programme) and NISP (National Industrial Symbiosis Programme). The project also created and implemented a bespoke project materials procurement policy to ensure the supply chain signed up to legal and responsible sourcing of materials. We also ensured our supply chain held Environmental Management Certificates to ISO 14001 or BES 6001 or equivalent.

Keeping traffic off Birmingham's streets

Working around an operational railway is a challenge in itself; however it also provides a very accessible resource that the project team uses to transport material into and from site, without having to use carbon intensive lorries around the busy city centre. Every week, a special train made two journeys into the construction site from a logistics depot in Bordesley on the outskirts of the city, keeping 10,000 lorry journeys off Birmingham's roads throughout the life of the project.

Energy

The expansion of the station concourse and additional lifts and escalators created demand for almost double the power consumption. In 2009 Network Rail commissioned the lead design and engineering consultant Atkins to carry out a Low and Zero Carbon (LZC) study for the project.

Before pursuing renewable technology it is imperative that the existing building fabric is improved, but one disadvantage of using the 1960's station façade was that it became very costly to improve, with long payback times and an unviable business case. New areas of the façade were built in accordance with current Part L of the Building Regulations.

The CHP plant is craned into position on the station roof.

District Heating Scheme pipework being installed in New Street.

Reaping the benefits of sunshine in Birmingham on the roof of the Lamp Block.

Network Rail worked closely with Atkins to make the main concourse area naturally ventilated to minimise energy usage. Computational Fluid Dynamic (CFD) modelling was carried out to ensure the new atrium worked effectively by extracting warm air in the summer using the stack effect, and preventing the station concourse from becoming too cold in the winter; some seating and waiting areas were installed with radiant heating panels as a result of the modelling.

Various renewable and low carbon technologies were explored, ranging from ground source heat pumps and biomass boilers, to photovoltaic (PV) cells to cover 2,000m^2 around the south of the station façade. The existing city centre location meant special constraints excluded the use of many technologies such as biomass and wind.

Photovoltaic cells were discounted when the John Lewis development was added to the south of the station, removing the proposed installation area. Network Rail then actively pursued the option of a Combined Heat & Power (CHP) scheme to provide the station with electricity from gas, and examined options to connect into the local district heating network to the north of the station. This reduces carbon emissions from on-site micro generation compared to traditional power station-generated grid electricity, reduces transmission losses and uses the waste by-product - heat - that is normally lost in the cooling towers of power stations. The preferred bidder, Cofely, was also very keen to use the subterranean network beneath the station to supply the south of the city and avoid disruption around the city centre.

The dilemma for Network Rail in using a CHP system was that the station demand profile required more electricity than heat, in a ratio of around 8:1. A heat consumption partner was required to utilise the surplus heat generated from the CHP plant, and John Lewis proved an ideal candidate, being attached to the south of the station with its biggest store outside London.

When John Lewis agreed to enter a heat agreement with Cofely, a carefully co-ordinated arrangement was created that required simultaneous signing of Energy Supply Contracts.

Once key partners and an outline scheme were identified, the major challenges of finding a location for the proposed 1.6MWe engine, and planning pipework routes through the station and John Lewis, without disrupting the complex programme of works around the station redevelopment, proved a key challenge. Identifying the plant location to satisfy The Clean Air Act and avoiding constructing a large chimney stack to satisfy local planning was just one of many obstacles the team overcame in pursuing low carbon technologies.

Lighting and Controls

All lighting was changed to low energy LEDs, and lighting controls were significantly improved to ensure lights turn off in back of house areas during prolonged unoccupied periods, and are dimmed in public areas when passengers are not present. All lighting is centrally controlled and monitored via a Building Management System (BMS) based in the station control room.

Water

The project minimised the consumption of potable water by the use of dual flush cisterns in all toilets along with low flow sensor taps. All water consumption is monitored via the BMS and a leak detection system also produces alarms in the control room if the event of any leakage. The project also constructed a large 100m³ rainwater collection tank to collect clean rainwater from the roof and façade and provide for more than 60% of the station's toilet flushing demand and irrigation for planting.

Other attenuation tanks were installed to prevent flooding overwhelming the main local sewer during periods of intense rainfall, to anticipate any future impact of climate change and increased risk of flooding in the city.

The Green Wall provides a focal point on the Moor Street Link walkway.

Materials

Sourcing materials with a low environmental impact was also a key consideration. Processes introduced on the project at an early stage ensured suppliers and contractors utilised responsibly sourced materials to ISO 14001 or equivalent and legally sourced all timber to FSC and PEFC standards. The project actively researched alternative materials and sourced carpet tiles from Miliken using yarn made from recycled fishing nets and the base from recycled off cuts from car seats.

Land Use and Ecology

Despite the New Street location having a low ecology site, Network Rail appointed qualified ecologists to advise and report on enhancing and protecting any ecological value. A key feature of the output was a 325 m² green wall along the Moor Street link to the east of the new station, with over 25 different species creating a completely new welcoming route into the station and concealing a long dark and dirty retaining wall.

Delivering the first BREEAM excellent modular building in a live rail environment – the Lamp Block

The project delivered a new and very green office building on the west end of platform one for our colleagues at Cross Country Trains, known as the Lamp Block after one of the earlier buildings on the site. With a green roof, solar photovoltaic panels to generate power, and solar thermal panels for hot water the building achieved a BREEAM rating of 'Excellent'.

The challenging brief was to provide a 1,000m² office accommodation building for train crew within a year of starting on site, in a challenging live rail environment with restricted site access in the middle of the city. The brief was to also deliver a BREEAM Excellent rated building. This led to several innovations including the first green roof in a live rail environment, the first BREEAM Excellent rated building within a railway station, with high recycled material rates from waste, and a reduction of more than 10% in carbon emissions from renewables.

An innovative modular construction method was used to fit with the location of the site, the constraints of limited working space and a very challenging delivery programme. The building was completed in a number of sections, waterproofed, then fitted out to considerably reduce the construction delivery programme.

These challenges led to the following innovations:

- Bespoke modules were fabricated and placed at a large radius from the site. All module loads were within the crane's safe working capacity. More conventional methods of construction were considered but could not deliver within the timescales imposed in the scope.
- All crane lifts carried out within railway possessions limited to a maximum seven hour period on Saturday evenings, in order to adhere to stringent safety criteria and mitigate any risk to the overhead line and rail station operations.

- Drop zones were created from the platform work site into an obsolete tunnel lying directly beneath. This was utilised to transit demolition and groundwork waste, being removed from the station by electric buggies and carts.
- The north side of the building was built into a sandstone outcrop, which was stabilised using 4m rock pins and shotcrete encapsulation. The rock stabilisation works were carried out in parallel with the construction of the superstructure.

These initiatives led to successful completion of construction works and delivery of the project without any incidents affecting the live rail network adjacent to the site.

Start & finish dates

GRIP 3 & 4 workshops (RIBA C/D)– April & May 2011
BREEAM pre-assessment – May 2011
GRIP 4 submission (RIBA D stage) – June 2011
Deconstruct existing Lampblock – August 2011
BREEAM Excellent (Design Interim stage) – July 12
Construction period Aug 2011 – May 2012
Cross Country move in – 2nd June 2012

The Team

Client: Network Rail
Tenant: Cross Country Trains
Delivery Project Manager: Mace (Matt Hempstock)
Construction Manager: Mace (Paul Gaffney)
Principal Contractor: Mace
GRIP 4 (RIBA C/D) Design: WSP
Design Interfaces: Atkins
Design Project Manager and Sustainability Manager: Mace (Azhar Quaiyoom)
D&B Main Contractor: Spencer Ltd
Main modular building construction contractor: Caledonian
Sub Structure/Groundworks Contractor: MPB
Demolition Contractor: Coleman & Co

Innovation in Sustainability

The Lamp Block accommodation building contains many items of green technology and sustainable construction practices implemented from the outset by early incorporation into the scheme design, and a procurement process designed to create a more sustainable development. Many of the items incorporated were a first for a building within the railway environment. The Lamp Block also incorporated many innovative initiatives in the design to offset carbon emissions by incorporating the following:

- **Solar panels** for electricity generation (photovoltaic panels) – located on the roof; these panels generate electricity to assist in powering the lighting and small power load of the building
- **Solar Thermal tubes** – again located on the roof, the tubes absorb heat and transfer the energy for supplementing the hot water demand, with the boiler used as a top up and secondary source
- **Sub metering** – to monitor the different energy demands such as lighting / heating and cooling circuits so there is more visibility on where energy is being used
- **Leak detection** – to inform the building maintainer if there are any leaks in the refrigerant system that may harm the atmosphere and water loss due to leakage
- **Monitoring and setting targets for CO_2 emissions** for transport to and from the site
- **Use of energy efficient and LED lighting** to reduce energy consumption, with lighting controls to avoid them being left on during unoccupied periods, in addition to dimming in daylight
- **Sheltered and well lit secure cyclist facilities** – to encourage building users to cycle to the workplace
- **Dual flush toilets and low capacity cisterns along with low water use taps and showers** – to minimise consumption of water

- Ensuring 80% of **materials have been responsibly sourced and timber legally sourced** – ensuring all timber has FSC or PEFC certification
- Ensuring the **supply chain has an environmental management system** in place – preferably ISO 14001 or equivalent
- Ensuring **non-hazardous construction and demolition waste was re-used and recycled** at a rate of over 85%

This renewable technology offset over 10% of the building's operational carbon emissions.

The building received a BREEAM design stage 'Excellent' rating, a first for a building within the railway environment and adjacent to platform and received a final 'Excellent' certification.

From an ecological prospective, the building houses a 'green roof' that contains over 14 different species to enhance the local ecology. Again this is a first in the railway environment, and also assists the drainage system from being overburdened by providing attenuation from heavy rain. In addition to minimising flood risks from new developments, we have installed attenuation tanks that capture any sudden surges in storm water and delays input into the main sewer to prevent any flash floods.

On site contractors used responsibly sourced materials and legally sourced timber, and were required to have environmental management systems in place. Waste produced from demolition works and packaging on site achieved high recycled/re-used rates in excess of 90%.

This project set a new precedent for railway buildings across the network and a good practice delivery benchmark for Network Rail. It changed the culture by creating awareness of sustainable buildings within the organisation. The project also created a realisation in the wider organisation and rail sector that despite the challenges of working in a live rail environment with tight deadlines and within a limited work area, sustainable buildings can be delivered using innovative methods of construction.

CASE STUDY

Geoff Inskip, Chief Executive, Centro

Centro & Gateway
by Geoff Inskip

An integrated passenger transport network is vital to the economy of the West Midlands, making an important contribution to jobs and growth in the region. Birmingham is a vibrant place, attracting more and higher quality jobs and growing to embrace new exciting neighbourhoods such as Eastside, Digbeth and Southside. This growth in business, housing and leisure is leading to many more trips into the city centre everyday and it is only fitting that New Street station has a world class facelift to accommodate our passengers and give them a first class customer experience.

Centro's role in the West Midlands

As Centro is responsible for the delivery of public transport in the West Midlands it was right that we became a partner in the project. This complements our aim to create a world-class public transport network delivered by a best in class organisation, representing the seven Metropolitan councils of the West Midlands: Birmingham, Coventry, Dudley, Sandwell, Solihull, Walsall and Wolverhampton.

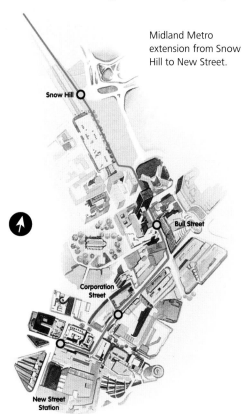

Midland Metro extension from Snow Hill to New Street.

In partnership with these authorities, Centro works to ensure everyone benefits from an effective transport system that meets the economic and environmental needs of the region, as well as providing access to jobs, finding innovative ways to help reduce congestion and offering seamless connections for people and goods to home and overseas markets. Many passengers from the wider travel to work area will use Birmingham New Street station taking advantage of the 12 refurbished platforms and new concourse enclosed by a giant atrium, allowing natural light to penetrate throughout the station. The new concourse is five times bigger, giving more space for the 170,000 passengers who use the station every day.

We deliver in a complex and dynamic environment, illustrated by the future arrival of HS2 at a new Curzon Street station with many passengers interchanging between Grand Central, Birmingham New Street and HS2. There is a need for a comprehensive Metro and Sprint network that will make these connections, the provision of which is recognised by business and civic partners alike.

The Importance of Public Transport in the West Midlands

The West Midlands, as a key hub of UK Plc, is focusing on sustainable economic growth to meet central government's growth agenda, developing the skills base to capitalise on global opportunities and building homes to meet the demand of those new jobs the region will create. Transport in the West Midlands is vital to achieving the connectivity needed to connect people to jobs, education, health, goods and services both nationally and internationally.

The West Midlands will achieve competitiveness in the global market through strong access to ports and airports and, looking to the future, the benefits to the region provided by HS2. Birmingham New Street will add to the world class feel of the city making it a place where people and companies want to come and do business.

Our continued investment in the public transport network, as set out in *Birmingham Connected*, will also:

- Make better use of existing transport assets, be they highways or rail networks
- Increase capacity and use of space-efficient public transport and environmentally friendly ways of travelling such as walking and cycling
- Locate new developments sensibly where they can be well-served by public transport
- Reduce some targeted demand for travel through measures such as multi-purpose journeys, car-sharing and home working
- Make public transport services more accessible to vulnerable groups
- Ensure proper access to public transport by walking and cycling

It is also essential that the region's needs, both now and in the future, are fully understood in terms of the requirements for improved public transport.

Midland Metro tram leaves the new terminus in Stephenson Street.

The redevelopment of Birmingham New Street station fits well into this agenda, providing the growth potential, connectivity and facilities appropriate for a transport hub at the heart of the West Midlands and at the centre of the nation's transport network, with a look and feel which provides a 'Gateway' fit for Birmingham and the rest of the West Midlands region in the 21st Century. Catering for the projected growth in rail passengers also provides a considerable opportunity to increase modal shift from the car to public transport, thus providing wider traffic benefits on the region's road network.

Factors behind Centro's funding contribution to the scheme

Centro has been engaged with the scheme from the initial inception meeting in 2002, following a call to arms from the then Chairman of the Strategic Rail Authority for West Midlands, particularly to the City of Birmingham, Advantage West Midlands and Centro, to take ownership of and champion the redevelopment of the station and work in partnership with Network Rail to bring about the changes essential to Birmingham New Street station's future.

Centro positioned itself as the passenger's champion, representing the interests of the West Midlands' public transport users to ensure that the redeveloped station met their needs during construction, at opening and into the future, including provision of long-term passenger capacity and improved interchange within the station and with other modes of transport, including bus and Metro.

At this time other city centre public transport schemes led by Centro were at the planning stage (including the Midland Metro extension from Snow Hill to New Street, new bus rapid transit (Sprint) routes and the creation of five transport interchanges at Snow Hill Station, Bull Street/Priory Queensway, Moor Street, Paradise Circus and New Street, to serve the entire West Midlands region). It was essential for Centro to be involved in the Gateway scheme to provide the integration and co-ordination needed to minimise disruption and maximise the benefits provided by all these initiatives to the city and wider West Midlands.

Centro's funding contribution to the project was therefore based on delivering these objectives and included:

Midland Metro tram heads into the street from Birmingham Snow Hill.

• Improved pedestrian link connecting the new station entrance and Metro stop in Stephenson Place with Moor Street station and Bus Mall via a new bridge (the Moor Street Link), constructed between the north east of the station and Worcester Street, adjacent to the Rotunda
• Enhanced passenger information, including real-time, train platform and destination information
• Improved directional signage to aid interchange and onward journeys into the city centre and wider West Midlands area
• Pick-up and set-down facilities for both private cars and taxis
• Cycle facilities and cycle access
• Provision of a new Centro Travel Shop
• Integration and co-ordination of the design to cater for the extension of Metro's City Centre Extension and other transport projects.

Interchange and Connectivity

An efficient transport network, including good interchange and connectivity, is integral to supporting growth and regeneration and essential to making public transport an attractive alternative to the car. Birmingham and the West Midlands are in an ideal location to be a successful well connected region, served as it is by extensive rail, road and air links. While the region benefits from a range of excellent transport connections, the quality of the transport environment and the connectivity of the transport network are in need of continual review and improvement. Along with Birmingham Gateway, a number of major transport improvements have been, or are being delivered, including the extension of the runway at Birmingham International Airport to cater for long haul flights and, in the longer-term HS2, which will enhance international access to the region from Europe and the rest of the world.

The Birmingham Gateway project plays a valuable part in supporting growth and regeneration by improving interchange between rail services, rail and other transport modes and providing better connectivity to the city centre by integrating directional signage within the station through Birmingham City Council's 'Interconnect' project. The new North-South route through the station removes the barrier across the city posed by the old station, evidenced by increasing interest by property developers in sites south of the station.

It also provides a dramatically improved arrival experience into the city and the wider West Midlands.

Corporation Street tram stop.

Rail to Rail

Birmingham New Street is one of the busiest interchange stations in Europe. At the heart of the rail network it is key to the performance of the train operating companies which utilise New Street for their services.

Gateway has provided a step change in the quality of the environment and ease of interchange between local and regional services through better permeability between platform and concourse, interchange signage, real-time information and waiting facilities, including retail outlets, making the experience of changing at New Street as convenient and pleasant as possible.

Rail to Metro

The design of Gateway was developed to take account of the Metro extension to New Street station. A Metro stop has been constructed at the North-West entrance to the station, thus creating an important link between light and heavy rail which will not only connect the Jewellery Quarter, but also in the future Broad Street, Five Ways and Digbeth. Centro is currently working with Birmingham City Council and other partners to develop the Digbeth Metro extension to connect New Street with the new HS2 Curzon Street station, providing a quick and easy link to high speed rail services to London.

Site poster, Midland Metro works, Birmingham New Street.

Rail to Bus

85% of all public transport journeys are made by bus, making it one of the most important modes of transport in the region. Improved permeability through the station allows better access to the main concentrations of bus stops within the city.

Rail to Taxis

Taxis play a key role in the onward journeys of many rail passengers, in particular business travellers, wishing to gain access to the Colmore Business District, the National Indoor Arena and other key business and leisure destinations throughout the region. The Gateway scheme has provided segregated drop-off and pick-up areas.

Rail to Cycling

The growth in cycling as a sustainable alternative to the car and public transport is important to the regional green and health agendas. The project has provided additional cycle storage facilities to encourage greater cycle use by rail users accessing the rail network and by station and railway staff. The redevelopment also opens up new cycle routes across the city.

When considered in conjunction with other cycle improvements across the city and wider region, i.e. Brompton Docks in the city centre and Centro's Cycle Hubs at key stations across the local rail network, the facilities at Birmingham New Street contribute to substantial betterment in cycling facilities in and around the station and across the region.

Midland Metro tram passes City Plaza in Corporation Street.

Rail to Walking

A key objective for the Gateway project was to improve pedestrian access routes to and from the station

An exciting future: the proposed extension to the HS2 terminus at Curzon Street.

thus reducing onward journey times to destinations in the city centre. The redevelopment of the station has removed pinch points and barriers which previously hampered the free flow of pedestrian movement in and around the station, opening up new walking routes across the city centre.

The future of public transport in the West Midlands

Midlands Connect

Midlands Connect is an ambitious initiative to identify and realise the transport connectivity improvements that the Midlands needs in order to maximise long-term regional economic growth.

The initiative draws upon and supports the strategic planning processes led by Network Rail and the Highways Agency for the national rail network and strategic road network, as well as Birmingham Airport's growth aspirations.

Midlands Connect's goal is to both support and influence these long-term planning processes and secure the necessary strategic investment in the Midlands's transport infrastructure.

New Strategic Transport Plan for the West Midlands

The Integrated Transport Authority is currently developing a new strategic plan for the future development of transport within the West Midlands which will:

- Give a bold vision with clear and very simple to understand messages about what the strategy is about
- Show how this plan clearly supports economic growth
- Be commonly accepted as the long-term plan for transport serving the West Midlands Metropolitan Area
- Show clearly how it fits with all the other strategies and plans in the region, particularly Midlands Connect and the HS2 Growth Strategy
- Major on the West Midlands becoming a world centre of smart mobility innovation and delivery
- Show how the region will deliver incremental, momentum-gathering improvements in line with the long-term approach, recognising attention to detail with small scale measures is important, alongside larger scale schemes
- Have a unique selling-point compared to other similar transport plans currently being produced in the UK
- Get buy-in to the bold vision and incremental, momentum-building approach to delivering it, with a practical approach to local funding which can be developed further over time
- Show how the plan has an approach for transport serving the West Midlands Metropolitan Area and work in partnership with neighbouring authorities and delivery agents for movements which cross administrative boundaries
- Set out clearly why the long-term approach chosen is the best one for the West Midlands Metropolitan Area to deliver economic growth, housing development, clean air, public health aims and economic inclusion
- Give increased prominence to short journeys and the role of public transport, cycling and walking to serve these more effectively.

Vision of the future: HS2 will place Birmingham at the heart of a new high speed rail network.

Laying the foundation for the tram extension across Great Charles Street Queensway.

The Station Manager's perspective by Steve Lewis

Managing a station like Birmingham New Street is challenging! As someone with experience of managing several large London termini, I expected that coming to Birmingham would be a very different experience. The sheer volume of commuter traffic makes managing a London station a twice daily challenge, but this is simply not comparable to New Street. Here everyone arrives on trains from one direction, gets off and then waits to board trains often going back out in the same direction; managing a London station is so much simpler than the busiest interchange station in the country, going through one of the most complex redevelopments ever seen in the station environment.

One thing that became instantly apparent to me was that the conventional station structure was not going to work in this environment. Traditionally stations are managed by a Station Manager and Duty Managers who are responsible for all station operations and safety compliance.

The complexities of the Gateway project were such that multiple alterations and revisions of contingency plans were required on an almost weekly basis. This, coupled with staff and stakeholder briefings of such alterations, meant a change to the structure of the station management team was required, even if that were to be only temporary. This was to be my second notable action, as two months after my arrival the old station closed for the 'Half Time' switchover.

Switchover

On Sunday April 28th 2013 the first portion of the redeveloped station opened to the public in what proved to be a relatively seamless transition. Never before has the metaphor relating to the stillness of the swan been more relevant. In the months leading up to the switchover the project had been managed extremely well, with Mark Bennett devising a 200 point plan to ensure safety compliance, staff familiarity of plans and environments, testing of the new working arrangements, stakeholder engagement and familiarity with the new station for customers. No matter how much planning takes place, there will always be unforeseen events and in anticipation of this we planned a control and command structure combining project, station and operational representatives.

Left: Antonia Waugh opens up the new station, whilst Jodie Merrick and Malcolm Burke help out at platform level (bottom right).

Above: Kully Uppal, CrossCountry Trains

Below: Andy McGann, Virgin Trains

On the Saturday night I was the station representative and oversaw the movement of equipment from the old station working environment to the new, the operational readiness of the station teams' new facilities and anything else that cropped up during the night. One thing that will stay with me forever is just how far from completion the new station seemed to be when we arrived on site. There were to my mind significant parts of the station remaining to be finished, including all of the floor paving at what was to be the new main entrance. I remember asking a project manager if he really thought it was going to be ready to open in less than 12 hours and he assured me it would. Over 1,000 operatives were on site that night and all worked amazingly. It ended up being one of the best nights in my career and saw station operators and construction operatives coming together to make things work. My teams were building furniture whilst construction operatives were worrying about passenger services and perceptions when we opened. It really was a wonderful example of everyone wanting to achieve the right outcome.

That morning we opened the new doors to the waiting public and watched the confused faces of people who'd missed the last train earlier in the morning and had gone back to the pub. They couldn't understand how the overnight transition from old to new station had taken place, or where the new facilities had come from.

In the days that followed I never tired of customers repeatedly asking questions such as "When did all this get built then?"

The station team

With the first part of the new station had been open and bedded in, my next task was to put a team structure in place that allowed us to cope with the challenges that the Gateway project continued to bring, whilst ensuring the operational

Below top to bottom:

Les Culverwell, Network Rail

Martin Wheelan, Network Rail

Stuart Warner, Network Rail

Uzmar Naz and Gayle Pardoe, Virgin Trains

station ran as smoothly as it could. The station had inherited organization structures from the old station era and was out of line with the agreed corporate template. This left us with two tiers of management in place. I was therefore able to conduct a review of all tasks required and create a revised structure to create a dedicated team of people to manage day to day operations, and a separate team to work with the Gateway project and examine how future enhancements to the station could be made to improve the overall customer experience. It was always my view that whilst the project delivered an iconic building, it would be the ongoing service that customers were offered that would make or break the lasting impression of the station. Experience has shown that people get used to nice new buildings quickly but if the service they receive remains exactly the same as it always was, then overall customer satisfaction will not sustainably rise.

To that end, my team was focused as much on project delivery as they were customer service enhancements. It was this structure that allowed the creativity to come up with a new national uniform for Network Rail station staff, new customer service training, a radically new approach to acquiring additional resource for customer service; and a programme of entertainment events that would make Birmingham New Street stand out from all other transport hubs.

Noise

You can't make an omelette without breaking eggs and you can't demolish an old building and remove over 30,000 tons of concrete without making some noise.

This was one of the two biggest challenges we had during the Gateway project. The difficult areas were the station platforms, where noise and vibration reverberated through the building structure combining with the ambient noise from passing trains, station announcements and air extract systems. This often meant that work was halted to avoid excessively noisy conditions for passengers, traincrew and dispatch staff whose working life is spent in these areas.

Noise can be subjective, and in order to ensure public and staff safety - as well as not delaying works unnecessarily - platform staff were provided with noise meters to measure background decibel levels and trained to understand the level at which they needed to report issues. When an area was found to be too noisy, work was halted and alternative methods of completing the task were agreed.

At the same time we undertook a noise survey across all platforms during periods when no construction activity was taking place. These results showed there were many things we could do to reduce general levels of noise and the resulting actions have led to a better environment for all concerned.

I'll always be grateful for the fantastic cooperative relationship between the station and platform operations teams. There was always a sense of wanting to work together for the greater good without which the teams would have been divided and in conflict, which could have led to energy being focussed in the wrong direction.

Congestion

Alongside noise, our other major concern was passenger congestion. The number of passengers using New Street continued to grow through the construction period and the interim station, with a limited number of stairs, escalators and lifts concentrated at one end of the platforms, changed the established method of dispersing passengers around the station.

This remained a primary concern for the station team throughout the second phase of the project works with, at times, tens of additional staff employed to assist customers to find their way around the station and to and from platforms. One such example was the management of the highly successful Birmingham Christmas Market, where we employed the services of crowd control experts with over 70 trained marshals to assist the station team to ensure we didn't let the platforms and trains become overcrowded.

The Christmas market was a huge draw and on its busiest day saw close to 300,000 people pass through the station on a single Saturday. I'm proud to say that during this time there wasn't a single reported accident and we managed to get everyone home safely.

Throughout these challenges the Gateway project and station team worked together to ensure public safety. There will always be conflicting objectives during large scale projects with important milestone achievements, cost drivers and high stakeholder expectations. However, it was always clear to me that public safety and train service performance was the number one priority for everyone involved no matter which team they were part of.

Launch plans

It was clear from the outset that the completion of the project and the opening of the finished station would be a major event. There are plenty of people interested in stations from a railway or architectural perspective, as well as those just curious to see what has been going on in the centre of the city for so long, so we knew there would be a huge amount of interest when a project of this scale is completed. Add to that the simultaneous opening of the Grand Central shopping centre and the excitement generated by the largest John Lewis department store outside of London, and it was clear this was going to be a big event.

I had without doubt the best team I've ever worked with to support me. The plan to ensure a safe and enjoyable launch of the new building was led by a key member of the team. One thing I've learnt about operating a station during such an extensive redevelopment was that you need to have a team of experts in many different fields; if you don't have such experts you need to find them and when you can't find them you need to create them. Craig Stenning became an expert in crowd management and event planning through a combination of his passion for the work and his willingness to learn. Craig became the most qualified person in the station community on this subject and went on to create an extremely robust plan.

This needed to ensure the safe access of people around the new station and shopping centre complex, to and from platforms and trains. No problem there, as Craig had already achieved this during other events, including the Christmas Market and Cheltenham races. However this plan also needed to ensure the capacity of Grand Central and John Lewis wasn't compromised and Craig devised a plan that involved a complex multi-stakeholder agreement to smooth the flow of people at the station level and control access to all areas of the building.

Top: Niasha Nugent, Network Rail

Above: Russell King, Network Rail

Below: Station war memorial

This needed approval from the emergency services and Birmingham City Council, which was achieved through a series of stakeholder planning meetings - led by Craig -that fed into a Steering Group looking at overall planning of the opening. Other considerations for this Group included the significant issue of local highways. Birmingham is enjoying a renaissance, with construction works across the city and multiple road closures planned as part of these wider regeneration plans. Whilst this is not ordinarily an issue for the railway station we knew that many John Lewis customers will arrive by car. With a 500 space car park being delivered as part of the Gateway project, we required a wider plan to ensure people had advance warning of where to park as they entered the city and navigated the many road closures and diversions that would be in place.

The plan was a complex beast and a testament to the hard work and dedication of everyone involved.

Conclusion

Being a key part of the Gateway project and of the city at that time has been the pinnacle of my career to date and afforded me learning I will take with me wherever I go in the future. I've always loved station management because of the enormous diversity in the role and I feel truly blessed to have been part of something as hugely impacting and important as the Birmingham Gateway project. None of this hugely complex project could have been delivered without an extraordinary degree of cooperation between multiple stakeholders to allow the station to operate safely through the lengthy construction period. The Birmingham New Street station team has been remarkably resilient and supportive, meeting a succession of challenges in difficult working conditions. It has been a privilege to lead this team, who have played such a key role in ensuring the success of the Gateway project.

The final shift, Saturday 27th April 2013

Passengers leave the old concourse for the last time as it closes for business and Patrick Power locks the door for the last time.

The British Transport Police team pose for a final photo as the construction team moves in.

Below: The station team of Steve Lewis, George Birtles, Neena Naylor, Glyn Tinsley, Nicky Walton, Alan Haskins, Ian Lynch, Taiyyib Talab, Mohammed Shafiq (Left), Stuart Warner, Patrick Power, Les Culverwell, Saghir Ahmed, Martin Whelan, Nikki Clynes and Alan Greenwood commemorate the last shift with a photo.

Ready for Business: Sunday 28th April 2013

The new station was ready for business the following morning after a hectic night's work.

Volunteers helped out as the station opened for business to ensure a smooth transition. Passengers soon adapted to the new layout.

Forming the core for the new John Lewis store, and grafting the structure on to the existing building.

John Lewis is excited about being a part of Birmingham, a city with rich industrial and creative history.

As well as being a part of Birmingham's creative future John Lewis will be adding to Birmingham's economic prosperity. John Lewis Birmingham will provide over 650 new jobs and deliver a legacy of real quality and value to the Greater Birmingham area.

John Lewis Birmingham

Birmingham has been a sought after location for John Lewis and fulfils a long-standing ambition of the business to bring its unique retail and employment offer to the city.

The position of the shop above New Street station, the busiest station outside London with an anticipated 52 million passengers a year travelling through it, gives John Lewis a unique opportunity to set a new benchmark in retailing.

The shop will be one of the most conveniently located shops in the country. Its station site also ensures that it is ideally located for commuters to collect purchases via johnlewis.com's Click & Collect service when going to and from the station.

This 250,000 sq ft shop is equivalent of three and a half football pitches and will be one of John Lewis's largest shops outside London; a new regional flagship.

The four storey shop will include all the latest retail concepts; 350,000 product lines including fashion, furniture, homewares, beauty and the latest technology. John Lewis Birmingham will be home to all the traditional services found in John Lewis department stores, as well as some added extras including; a Kuoni travel concession, a Foreign Exchange bureau, a Beauty Spa and a Clarins Skin Spa.

It is also the first full-line department store for John Lewis since John Lewis Stratford City opened in London in 2011. The opening of John Lewis Birmingham builds on the two convenience-driven shop formats at London's St Pancras station and Heathrow Airport Terminal 2 which opened in 2014.

As a part of John Lewis's unique Partnership structure, all new employees will become Partners and be co-owners of the business, as well as receiving a host of benefits, including an annual bonus, access to holiday and leisure facilities, education and career development support.

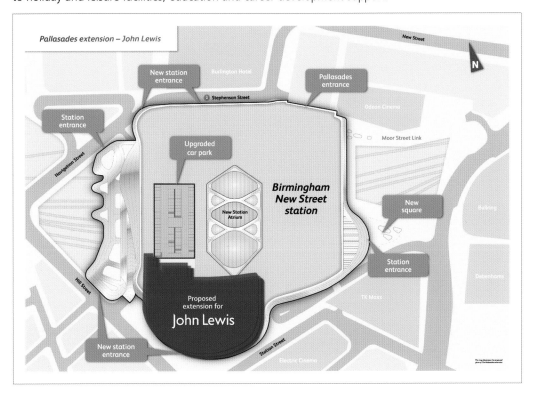

John Lewis construction

John Lewis announces its presence across the atrium roof.

Lisa Williams, originally from Birmingham, will be Head of Branch at John Lewis Birmingham and had hoped for a long time that the retailer would open a shop in her home city. "To be asked to run this shop is a dream come true and for me it's a homecoming to my friends and family after many years away", she says. "There's massive excitement and energy about John Lewis coming to the city and the community. 2015 is a hugely exciting year for Birmingham and we are thrilled to be opening our new shop at this time. I can't wait to welcome our new Partners into the team."

Our involvement in the community

In Birmingham, like all communities where John Lewis operates, the Company is committed to being involved in the community, forging close links between Partners (employees), schools, charities and local authorities.

John Lewis Birmingham will provide both volunteering time and financial assistance to support local initiatives through Community Matters a charitable giving scheme.

Handover of the store to John Lewis L-R Sir Albert Bore (Birmingham City Council), Jeremy Collins (John Lewis), Sir David Higgins (Network Rail), Mark Reynolds (Mace).

Pallasades to Grand Central by Jonathan Cheetham

Birmingham was known as the motor city, at the heart of the automotive industry and an industrial powerhouse with one of the highest paid blue-collar workforces in the country. Already recognised as the 'capital city' of the Midlands, the city was undergoing wholesale development, slum clearances and new builds throughout the late 50s and early 60s.

As part of these developments, Birmingham's rail hub, New Street station, was seen by developers as an opportunity to rebuild and improve the existing facility. Design commenced for the original shopping centre in the early 60s, as a new build to be constructed on top of the railway station. Set atop enormous piles, driven into the landscape surrounding the railway tracks, this was seen as transformational and a cutting edge build. This culminated with the opening in 1971 of 290,000 square feet of selling space, known as the 'Birmingham Shopping Centre.'

The centre proved extremely popular and due to having the shortest connection into the city from the railway station, enjoyed some of the highest footfall in the country, as commuters streamed in and out on a daily basis. At the very

Jonathan Cheetham

heart of the city and linked to the original Bullring, the centre was the first point of access into the city and become known as the gateway to Birmingham. The Birmingham offices for Norwich Union (who were the original owners) were situated at the top of the building above the mall level.

The Birmingham Shopping centre became the first port of call for shoppers as the newest development in the city and the fountain in the centre became a focal point for people to meet. The centre had uniformed personnel with Alsatian dogs regularly patrolling the mall and eight dogs were housed permanently in kennels on the roof servicing deck of the building, a far cry from today's customer service

standards. Despite these canine guards, mischievous patrons caused mountains of bubbles much to the chagrin of the management and security team by regularly dosing the fountain with washing up liquid.

In 1987, the centre was given a new lease of life re-inventing itself as The Pallasades, having received some minor shop fitting and physical improvements to create a lighter, brighter more harmonised environment, to encourage customers to spend more time within the centre. The Pallasades was home to 80 eclectic units of mainly convenience shopping, with a mix of discounted shops and 'grab and go' food brands. It was the place in the city where great buys and value for money were always available. From accessories, gifts, and fashion to electrical, sports and beauty wares. With big brands such as Woolworths, Argos, Tesco Express and Poundland plus a complementary range of smaller specialist independent shops, the centre catered for the value driven customer. Purchased in 1998 by Capital & Regional (C&R) Properties, the building and interior received some much needed care and investment and became the flagship property of the newly created subsidiary of C&R, The Mall Ltd Partnership.

Under the Malls stewardship, the vitality of the centre was restored, helped by improving and refurbishing the escalators, an entry point between the centre and the station (known locally as "the mouse hole").

The closure of the old Bullring markets for the development and rebuild of the new Bullring, left the Pallasades as the dominant business within the city for a period of 3 years until the reopening of Bullring in September 2003.

Customers were loyal to the Pallasades, with the centre playing a large part in the local community, initiating and supporting numerous local initiatives including Local Heroes, Baby of the Year and the local Schools Awards all of which still continue.

The Pallasades provided the first point of entry to the city centre and situated above New Street station was commonly regarded as "the gateway to the city". The centre average weekly footfall was over 420,000 per week welcoming customers through the main entrance from New Street up 'the ramp' with further access available from Station Street and Stephenson Street. The centre was the shortest covered route to Bullring having a connection to this centre via an aerial link connecting the two buildings.

In 2005, The Mall sold the property to Warner Estate Holdings who became victims of the economic and banking malaise of 2008, with Warner selling the estate to Birmingham City Council for a net loss in excess of £45M, helping to speed the demise of their business.

Today, the Pallasades has been redeveloped into a modern retail and leisure environment – Grand Central Birmingham. The name denotes the next exciting chapter in shopping opportunities within Birmingham and will see the redeveloped scheme become an integral landmark to the city as part of

The 'mousehole' escalators provided a link between the Pallasades and the station. Grand Central provides a dramatically improved shopping environment (opposite).

The Grand Central logo rises above the eastern façade (top). The atrium and main concourse form a centrepiece to Grand Central (below).

the transformation of New Street station. This enhancement is a pivotal landmark in the aspirations for continuous improvement laid out in "The Big City Plan", the long term visioning document to guide, encourage and support as an aid to the greater regeneration of the world-class city of Birmingham.

Highly reflective cladding to give an iconic stamp to the building has unified the exterior. Key to Grand Central Birmingham's transformation is the addition of one of the biggest John Lewis stores in the UK with 250,000 sq. ft. over four levels. Alongside this sits a retail mix of unrivalled premium fashion, including such brands as Cath Kidston, The White Company, Kiehls and Giraffe plus an abundance of other quality retail and an exceptional and varied food offer.

These brands, many of which are newcomers to the city, alongside the state-of-the-art architecture, capped with a soaring atrium and a unified vision in the customer journey, will create a new and dynamic shopping experience in the heart of Birmingham. This positions Grand Central as an integral part of Birmingham's retail landscape and with the close integration alongside the world class New Street station, Grand Central Birmingham creates a truly unique shopping and travel destination and a meeting place for visitors to the city.

Destination Stations by David Biggs

Network Rail and station development

Network Rail owns and manages 18 of the largest stations in Great Britain and has invested significantly in developing their potential. Our vision for these managed stations is for them to be recognised as destinations in their own right – first class travel facilities which simplify the lives of the busy passenger and are a convenient environment for retail, leisure and business in the communities where they are situated.

David Biggs, Managing Director Property, Network Rail

Station users are informed, connected and experience-driven. They are drawn to stations for various reasons, shaped by whether they are commuters, long distance travellers, local residents or nearby workers. Their shopping habits have evolved through the decades. Consumers use many different ways to shop; combining online research with physical shopping and expecting to be able to collect their purchases across multiple locations. Our stations are changing along with their shifting needs and expectations; we consciously select our retail outlets, eateries and brands to reflect these changing customer needs, as we start to fully recognise our place as an important commercial touch point within the wider retail environment.

We estimate that more than one billion visitors will pass through our stations each year by 2020 and it is our duty to react and facilitate them by improving station environments, improving passenger satisfaction and generating increasing levels of sustainable income for reinvestment in rail.

Kings Cross

Below: Manchester
Piccadilly.

Bottom right: Balcony at
London Waterloo.

A bigger better and brighter station for Birmingham

Network Rail's Gateway scheme has transformed Birmingham New Street into a stunning transport hub for the West Midlands and, combined with the allied redevelopment of Grand Central shopping centre above the station, will create a world class transport, shopping and community hub in the heart of the city.

We work with leading brands and service providers to offer a compelling mix of categories, concepts, and formats which respond to customer needs. 16,000 square feet of new retail space has been created in Birmingham New Street, providing an amazing opportunity to bring our vision for station retail to one of the country's fastest growing cities. It will offer new shopping and dining facilities anchored by the largest John Lewis outside of London.

Meeting needs, exceeding expectations

The customer is at the heart of everything we do. We regularly commission consumer insight about station users and their behaviours, to find out if we are meeting their needs and what can be done to improve their experience. The findings of our research help us make informed decisions about the type of shops we open and the brands we work to meet the requirements of all station users.

Network Rail has 480 retail and catering units, representing 140 brands across our managed stations; each having been particularly selected for the consumer's needs.

Investment at stations such as King's Cross, Manchester Piccadilly and Waterloo demonstrates how, by delivering the right brands in the right formats, in the right place, we are changing perceptions of what modern railway stations can provide. Birmingham New Street enhances our portfolio further and provides a stunning example of how the station experience can be transformed to be fit for the 21st century.

Chris Montgomery, Project Director

Looking Back by Chris Montgomery

Completion of the project and opening of both the new station and shopping centre will be a very satisfying moment for me and the conclusion of an epic journey of a team in which I am extremely proud. To undertake the scale of works necessary on such a complicated project whilst keeping the station fully operational has been extraordinarily difficult.

I took over the reins to the project in 2009 from Martin Chambers who did a sterling job in steering the project through from a concept to a funded reality, and I formally thank him for this. Upon arrival one of the first pieces of work to commence was the removal of a whole floor of a multi storey car park directly above an operational railway. Many people explained that this would not be possible without closing the whole railway down, which made me realise just what the project was going to be like!

Some of the engineering solutions adopted when doing demolition or constructing the various elements have been breathtaking, and the building has seemed to throw up new surprises almost every week! If the project were not difficult enough we then (at the half-way point) decided to build a new department store on the side of the building, refurbish the shopping centre and demolish and rebuild the multi-storey car park on the roof of the building.

The amount of collaboration evident across the project has been immense, whether this was between contractors, stakeholders or neighbours. Working in a live, sub-surface station environment requires specific skills. From the outset, it was necessary to change the 'hearts and minds' of our contractors and their operatives to get them to operate in the correct manner. Mace are to be applauded for their work in this area to bring all the contractors to the same level.

One of the main reasons the project has been a success in terms of working alongside a live station has been the close relationship which developed between the station and the construction teams. In fact, for the last three years of the project they have acted as one and they all deserve congratulating on developing such mature relationships.

Looking back on the last six years there are many highlights to remember but I list here a few which bring me personal satisfaction:

- Maintaining an exemplary safety record whilst undertaking the most difficult and challenging project in such close proximity to the travelling public
- Taking Occupational Health to another level for all of the operatives and staff of our contractors and ourselves
- Seeing the brand new iconic structure and Atrium space emerge from the dark, dingy 1960's concrete cube that was the old station
- Creating job opportunities throughout the life of the project by working closely with colleges, etc. enabling over 120 apprentices to learn on the project
- The 'Entry into Service' work at the end of phase 1 which allowed us to seamlessly move a whole station 70m sideways overnight
- Receiving a personal letter from the Prime Minister thanking the whole team for their efforts and fantastic work
- Carrying out the works throughout the life of the project in a professional and safe manner

In conclusion I would like to thank all the staff who have lived and breathed the project for the past 6 years of construction work, the travelling public and the Train Operating companies and finally the Funders and the Network Rail Board who have supported the project throughout.

Above: Collecting the Excellence in Sustainability Award at the Chamber of Commerce awards 2015 – Emma Jesson, Martyn Woodhouse, Azhar Quaiyoom, Chris Montgomery and Greg Lowson (President, Birmingham Chamber of Commerce).

Left: The project celebrates getting its 100th apprentice.

Mike Whitby (former Leader of Birmingham City Council) launches the Birmingham Gateway Academy.

Prime Minister David Cameron stops to pose for 'selfies' with apprentices on his visit to the project in September 2014.

Overleaf: A station transformed; before and after plans of the concourse facilities.

Birmingham New Street
Station guide

NetworkRail

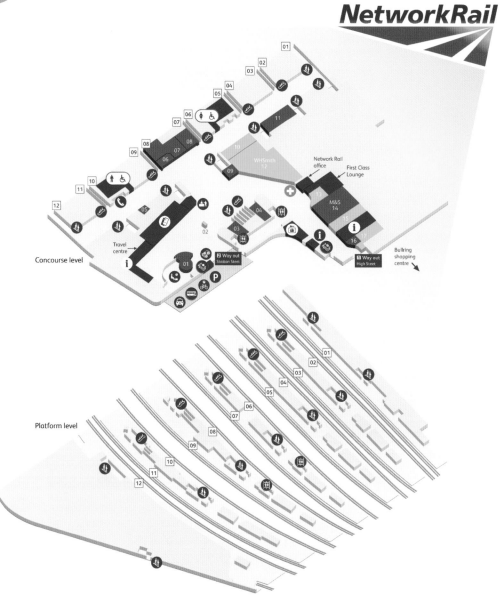

Concourse level

Platform level

Travel centre

Network Rail office

First Class Lounge

WHSmith 12

M&S 14

Way out Station Street

Way out High Street

Bullring shopping centre

⊙ You are here

Key	Food and Drink	Shopping
Accessible toilets	05. AMT Coffee	15. Boots
Baby change	03. Burger King	13. Cards Galore
Bike park	01. Caffe Ritazza	17. Coral
Bureau de change	07. Camdenn Food Co.	02. Photo-Me
Buses	16. Costa Coffee	10. WHSmith
Cash point	14. M&S Simply Food	12. WHSmith
Escalators	09. Millie's Cookies	
First aid	06. Pasty Shop	
Information	08. Upper Crust	
Left luggage	11. Shakespeare (Pub)	
Lift	04. Whistlestop	
Parking		
Platform numbers		
Stairs		
Station reception		
Taxis		
Telephones		
Tickets		
Toilets		
Waiting room		

*If you need help please
speak to one of our staff
or call the helpline on*
08457 11 41 41

Birmingham New Street
Station map

Snow Hill Station (1000m)

STEPHENSON STREET

Moor Street Station (600m)

Exit to Victoria Square

Grand Central

Local travel information

Ladywood House

01

02 Boots

24

25

1A

Virgin First Class Lounge

26 27

NAVIGATION STREET

Short stay P

1B

2B

3B

03

23

2A

3A

28

Grand Central and Bullring

22

4A

5A

29 30

04

4B

4C

05

5B

06 WHSmith

19

20

6A

7A

Exit to Smallbrook Queensway and Bullring

6B

7B

Ticket office

21

31

32

07

8B

9B

08 M&S Simply Food

18

8A

9A

Grand Central

33

09

10

Grand Central and Bullring

34

11

10B

11B

12

16

10A

11A

Multi-faith room

12B

15

17

12A

John Lewis Partnership (JLP)

13

John Lewis Partnership (JLP)

14

Southside

Entrance/Exit Southside

H3

H1 H2

HILL STREET

STATION STREET

Services and facilities

Accessible toilets		Parking	P
Baby change		Photo Booth	
British Transport Police		Platform numbers	01
Buses		Post Box	
Cash point		Ramp	
Changing place		Station reception	
Cycle park		Stairs	
Drop off point		Taxis	
Fast ticket machine		Telephones	
First aid		Tickets	
Information		Toilets	
Left luggage		Waiting room	
Lift			
Mobility assistance			

Food, drink and shopping

All Bar One	32	Oliver Bonas	29
Benugo	25 31	Pasty Shop	11
Boots	02	Pret A Manger	19
Camden Food Co.	04	Starbucks	12
Costa	05	Upper Crust	07
Delice de France	01	WHSmith	06
Five Guys	33		
Funky Pigeon	10		
HEMA	15		
Hotel Chocolat	26		
Joe's Coffee House	34		
Leon	21		
M&S Simply food	08		
Mi Casa Burritos	09		

If you need help please speak to one of our staff or call our helpline on

03457 11 41 41

networkrail.co.uk/
birmingham-new-street-station

 /BirminghamNewStreet
 @NetworkRailBHM

The Contractors

A1 Sheet Metal Flues Ltd

AG First Ltd

Alandale Logistics Ltd

Amey LG Limited

ANS Group (Europe) LLP

Atkins Ltd

Balfour Beatty Rail Civils

Balfour Beatty Rail Limited

BAM Nuttall Limited

Barhale Plc

Birchall

Briggs Amasco Ltd

C Spencer Limited

Clark & Fenn Skanska Limited

Coleman & Company Ltd

DGP Logistics PLC

DSM Demolition Ltd

Elliott Thomas Ltd

Energetics Design & Build Limited

Fabric Architecture Limited

Fireclad Limited

Glazzard (Dudley) Limited

Grants of Shoreditch Limited

Hewlett Civil Engineering Ltd

Infra Safety Services Labour Ltd

Irvine Whitlock Limited

John Doyle Construction Limited

Keltbray Limited

Lyndon Scaffolding plc

Martifer Construções Metalomec

Martifer UK Ltd

MECX Technical Services Ltd

Mouchel Ltd

MPB Structures Ltd

NG Bailey Limited

OCS Environmental Services Limited

Otis Limited

Protec Fire Detection plc

Robell Control Systems Ltd

SAS International Ltd

Sentinel Lightning Protection and Earthing

Shaylor Group Plc

Simco External Framing Solutions Ltd

Stannah Lift Services Limited

Swift Horsman Ltd

Thomas Vale Construction Ltd

Tyco Fire & Integrated Solutions (UK)

Vector Foiltec Limited

Vinci Construction UK Ltd

Visual Security Services UK Ltd

Volker Fitzpatrick Ltd

Waco UK Ltd

Watson Steel Structures Limited

Weir Waste Services Limited

Wquay Ltd

Wysepower Ltd